Victory for the Ops Room Girls

Vicki Beeby writes historical fiction about the friendships and loves of service women brought together by the Second World War. Her first job was as a civil engineer on a sewage treatment project, so things could only improve from there. Since then, she has worked as a maths teacher and education consultant before turning freelance to give herself more time to write. In her free time, when she can drag herself away from reading, she enjoys walking and travelling to far-off places by train. She lives in Shropshire in a house that doesn't contain nearly enough bookshelves.

Also by Vicki Beeby

The Women's Auxiliary Air Force

The Ops Room Girls
Christmas with the Ops Room Girls
Victory for the Ops Room Girls

VICKI BEEBY

Victory
for the
Ops Room
Girls

CANELO

First published in the United Kingdom in 2021 by

Canelo
31 Helen Road
Oxford OX2 0DF
United Kingdom

A CIP catalogue record for this book is available from the British Library.

Print ISBN 978 1 80032 205 9
Ebook ISBN 978 1 80032 204 2

Look for more great books at www.canelo.co

Printed and bound in Great Britain by Clays Ltd, Elcograf S.p.A.

1

For my family:

Mum

Duncan, Jana & Emma

Chris, Katka & Elena

Chapter One

Jess bounced on her toes outside the Mansion House at RAF Bentley Priory, gazing across the extensive grounds. All around her, groups of men and women dressed in RAF blue hurried past, some engaged in earnest discussion, others striding towards one building or other. There was an air of purpose about them that set Jess's pulse jangling. She could hardly believe she was here at last: Fighter Command Headquarters!

A rumble overhead made her stomach clench and she glanced up at the sky. Towering black clouds loomed to the west, threatening to blot out the afternoon sunshine. As she watched, the flicker of distant lightning lit the base of the clouds with a coppery glow. She forced herself to relax. It was just a distant storm, not a raid. Now the Allies were advancing across Europe, everyone was confident Britain had seen the last of the bombing raids. Nevertheless, she doubted she would ever forget the horror of huddling in a bomb shelter, listening to the whistle of falling bombs, praying none of them scored a direct hit. All tension faded when she saw what she had been watching for – a gleam of red hair beneath a WAAF officer's cap. Jess waved at the young woman who approached on the path from the main gate. The WAAF officer responded with an enthusiastic wave and quickened her pace.

'What time do you call this, Evie Bishop?' Jess called, the moment her friend was in earshot.

'Sorry.' Evie jogged the last few yards then clutched her sides, gasping. 'Got held up in the Filter Room, and it's uphill all the way from there.' Then she glanced at her watch and frowned. 'Wait. I said I'd meet you at 1630 hours. I'm five minutes early, you clot.'

'I never said you were late. Just asked for the time.'

Evie swatted her on the arm. The next moment they were hugging and laughing. Although they had met up as often as they could over the years, it wasn't nearly enough for Jess, who had missed her friend terribly.

'It's so good to see you, Jess,' Evie said in the end. 'I can't believe we'll be back working together after all this time.'

'I know. I keep having to look at my transfer orders to convince myself I'm not dreaming.' She had spent the last year and a half as a Filterer Officer at RAF Watnall in Nottinghamshire, arriving only a month after Evie had been transferred from there to Bentley Priory. It had been frustrating to miss her, and Jess had spent the year longing for a transfer either to Bentley Priory or Rudloe Manor near Bath, where their friend May Lidford was posted.

'Have you finished here?' Evie asked.

'Yup. I've been issued my passes, and I'm free until I report for duty tomorrow.'

'Great. I'll take you to the Mess. This way.' Evie started to walk down the path then glanced back, her eyes sparkling. 'By the way, you'll never guess who else is here. Quite the Amberton reunion.'

'Not old Hellerby?' Jess quailed as she followed Evie, remembering the flight officer who had kept Jess and her friends on their toes during the Battle of Britain.

Evie laughed. 'Last I heard, Ellerby was still striking terror into the hearts of the plotters at Amberton. Anyway, you've nothing to fear from Ellerby now you're an officer yourself.'

Jess glanced down at her sleeve and the wide single ring denoting her rank of Section Officer. She had been commissioned eighteen months ago as an Assistant Section Officer, thanks in part to the encouragement she had received from Flight Officer Jean Ellerby when she'd been a plotter at Amberton. Then six months ago, her superiors had declared themselves impressed with her work and promoted her to Section Officer. However, it was still hard to think of herself as an officer rather than a lowly Aircraftwoman second class, trying to win the approval of her superiors.

Evie gave her arm another tug. 'Anyway, come on. I'm talking about someone much more exciting than Ellerby. I said we'd meet her in the anteroom.'

To Jess's surprise, Evie didn't lead her to the Officers' Mess in the mansion house itself, but set off across the grounds.

'Where are we going?' Jess asked, casting a glance back towards the impressive mansion. In the fading sunlight, its pillared portico gleamed white, contrasting with the darkening sky. 'I thought you said we were going to the anteroom.' She thought longingly of the comfortable armchairs there were bound to be in the mess anteroom; after a long day of travel she was looking forward to taking the weight off her feet. When she had learned of her transfer, she had pictured a mess shared with the RAF officers, mixing with some of the most senior officers in the air force. But it looked like there must be a separate mess for the WAAF officers.

'We are. The one in No.2 WAAF Officers' Mess,' Evie replied. Then she added with a smile, 'It's a tidy step, but worth it.' And Jess was reminded of Evie's first day at Amberton, when Jess had been tasked with showing Evie and May around the base and taking them to the Waafery at High Chalk House. From Evie's smile, Jess knew her friend was remembering the same thing.

'Better than High Chalk House?' she asked. The WAAFs of RAF Amberton had loved the stately home that had been requisitioned to serve as their living quarters.

'Wait and see.'

'Hang on,' Jess said, her brain catching up with what Evie had said. 'No. 2 Mess – you mean there's more than one?'

Evie darted a quick glance behind them and lowered her voice. 'Those of us assigned to Special Duties are housed separately. I suppose the powers that be want to make certain we don't let slip the nature of our work after one too many glasses of wine.'

Jess felt a thrill at the reminder that here at Bentley Priory, she would be at the hub of Fighter Command and privy to a vast amount of secret information. As she followed Evie out of Bentley Priory and down Stanmore Hill she recalled the promise she, Evie and May had made at Brighton. They had just witnessed their wounded troops returning from the Dunkirk evacuation and for the first time the threat Britain faced had sunk in. At Evie's prompting, they had vowed to take their work seriously and make a difference to the war. That vow had been a constant presence at the back of Jess's mind, nudging her to keep going whenever she was tired or tempted to cut corners. Lives depended upon her. Now she was at Bentley Priory, the stakes had increased. The fact that the WAAFs who had signed the Official Secrets Act were separated from the others was a sign of the importance of their work.

Although Jess was a Londoner through and through, her usual haunts were the East End and the fashionable West End. She had never been on this side of London before and marvelled at the tree-lined street and the common as the strode on.

'Blimey,' she muttered to Evie as they passed a house set back from the road with an elegant gravelled drive and a huge tree-filled garden. 'A family of ten could get lost in there. I used to pity the poor people who lived right on the outskirts. How wrong I was!'

'A bit posh for the likes of us,' Evie said with a laugh. 'I prefer the centre of London, but I don't know it very well.'

'Good job you've got me as a friend,' Jess said. 'First chance we get, you and me'll have a night on the town.'

'Just you and me?'

'Oh. I suppose we can invite Alex if he's around.'

Evie gave Jess an understanding look. Too under-standing. 'That's not what I meant.'

'Who did you mean, then?'

'You'll see.' Evie turned up a driveway. 'Here we are.'

Jess only held back a whistle of surprise because it would be most unbecoming of an officer. They stood in the garden of a large house with a thatched roof that wouldn't look out of place in the West Sussex countryside. 'You're pulling my leg.'

Evie shook her head, grinning. 'Welcome to Bentley Manor. Makes up for losing High Chalk House, doesn't it?'

'I'll say.'

Evie led the way through the garden then into the house. Jess found herself in a large but cosy room, with timbered beams and a huge inglenook fireplace. This being August, there was no fire lit, but she could imagine how warm and welcoming the fire would be in the colder months. The walls were hung with pictures and the room was filled with comfortable armchairs that she longed to sink into.

'Come on then,' Jess said, only now remembering the comment Evie had made at Bentley Priory. 'Who's this person we're to meet?'

A young woman sprang to her feet from the depths of an armchair. She stood a head taller than the other women in the room, and her chestnut-brown hair gleamed in the electric light.

Jess stopped dead. 'May Lidford, as I live and breathe. When did you get here? I thought you were at Rudloe Manor.'

May hurried forward to give Jess an enthusiastic hug, then, as they settled into armchairs, May said, 'I know. I thought I'd be there for the duration, but my CO said they needed more Filterer Officers at 11 Group and recommended me. I wasn't going to pass up the chance of us being all together again.' There was barely a trace of the Birmingham twang that had prevented May from being posted as an Operations Room plotter when she had first joined the WAAF. Thanks to Jess's tuition, May now spoke with the BBC accent expected of any WAAF whose duty required her to give aircraft numbers and positions under pressure without being misunderstood.

'A reunion!' Jess looked at her two best friends, hardly able to believe they were together again. 'This calls for a celebration. Our first night off, we're going to hit the town.'

'Isn't it wonderful we're all together again?' Evie's eyes shone. 'For more than just a couple of days, I mean.'

'I know. And it will be the first time any of us have worked in the same place since May and I finished our RDF training,' Jess replied.

They had all served in various locations around Britain since then. After leaving Amberton, Jess and May had been trained to read the Range and Direction Finding – or RDF – system that sent radio beams out from Britain's coastline, picking up incoming aircraft as blips on the screens. Since the Americans had joined the war, people were starting to use their term for RDF – radar. Interpreting these blips to tell how many aircraft, how high they were and how far away, plus whether they were friend or foe had required great concentration and skill. After passing the course, Jess had spent three months working at a remote RDF station, known as a Chain Home station, in Cornwall, plus another four months in East Anglia before being recommended as a Filter Plotter and finally retraining as a Filterer Officer. Filter Plotters worked in the Filter Room of one of the Group headquarters of RAF Fighter Command, each group covering a set area of Britain. Filter Plotters received readings from a Chain Home station and plotted it on a map. Filterer Officers then analysed this data, filtering it to provide a detailed picture of all aircraft detected off the coast of Britain. This information was then sent to Operations Rooms in fighter stations around the country, where it was plotted by Operations Room plotters – the role both Evie and Jess had when they had first joined the WAAF. Jess had been fascinated to be involved in all aspects of the Chain Home system, and her experience meant that even Evie deferred to her sometimes when it came to questions about RDF.

Although they had managed to meet up every so often in the nearly four years since she and May had left Amberton, it had never been for more than forty-eight hours at a time. Their various duties had prevented them from getting any longer leaves together. Besides, Evie and May had understandably wanted to spend their longer leaves with Alex and Peter, their respective boyfriends who were both RAF pilots.

Jess shook off the wistful twinge that she always felt when she thought about being the only single one in the group. While Evie and May had never made her feel excluded, it was impossible not to be aware that they both had other priorities, that they would always put spending time with Alex and Peter first. Jess couldn't fault them for that. Even though the war was now going their way, pilots were being killed every day. It was only right that Evie and May would want to make the most of every precious moment with their boyfriends in case it was their last.

Jess eyed Evie thoughtfully. Her boyfriend, Alex, was the Squadron Leader of Brimstone Squadron, one of the fighter squadrons that had been based at Amberton when she had been there. The same squadron as Milan Mašek. Jess swallowed. Evie might have news of Milan. Jess had been seeing him while at Amberton but had broken up with him when she left. Despite knowing it was for all the right reasons, no other man she'd met in the intervening years could compare with him.

Evie glanced at her watch. 'Still an hour before dinner. Let's have a cup of tea and catch up.'

Once they had been provided with tea, they settled in their armchairs. Evie looked at Jess with a little tilt of the head. 'I hope you're not too disappointed not to have a shared Mess,' she said. 'It does have the advantage of being a little less formal than if we were sharing with the top brass.'

'Tell me about it,' said May. 'I was terrified when I started at Rudloe Manor.' This was the headquarters of 10 Group, near Bath. 'We had to eat under the eye of the great and the good and I hardly dared to eat in case I used the wrong fork and was hurled out of the Mess.'

'Speaking of the great and the good,' Jess said, with a nod towards Evie, 'how does it feel to be leader of your watch?'

Evie looked self-conscious. 'To be honest, I keep expecting the CO to wonder what possessed her to put me in charge.'

'She'll be thinking nothing of the sort. If she's got any sense, she'll think you're the best of the bunch.' Jess grinned at May. 'We'll need to be on our best behaviour from now on, Lidford. No slacking with Evie keeping her beady eye on us.'

'Do you suppose we'll see out the rest of the war together?' May asked.

'I hope so,' said Jess. 'Can't be long now the Allies are advancing. Won't be much for us to do except track our own lads as they cross and recross the Channel.'

Evie, however, looked doubtful. 'There are still the flying bombs,' she said. 'It's awful when we pick those up. There's very little we can do.'

'I thought we had them under control. I thought the anti-aircraft gunners could deal with them.'

'They do for the most part, but a few get past. That's not what worries me, though.'

At Evie's dark tones, Jess felt a chill of foreboding. 'What? Don't tell me London's still in danger.'

'I don't know. But there are all sorts of rumours about another secret weapon on the way. Bigger. Faster. Intelligence have definitely got wind of something, but no one knows quite what it is.'

A cold weight of dread settled in Jess's stomach. 'But I told my Auntie Vera it was safe to return home.' It had taken all her skills of persuasion to get Vera to move out of London during the Blitz and stay with a cousin in Wales. 'And she's bringing little Hannah with her.' If Evie was right, the two people most precious to her might be back in the firing line.

–

The dinner that followed in the mess should have been a celebration for Jess, reunited with her two best friends. Instead the food tasted like ashes. Somehow she had managed to find words to say to the twenty or so other off-duty WAAF officers that she'd been introduced to but she was sure she would be labelled the shy one instead of May. Thankfully, Evie and May hadn't seemed to notice anything was wrong. They chatted to their neighbours at the polished dining table, laughing at all the jokes as though they hadn't a care in the world. At any other time, Jess would have been proud of how May had conquered her shyness and joined in the conversation with confidence. Now, however, her overriding thoughts were of her Auntie Vera and Hannah. She would never forgive herself if they fell victim to some new weapon after she'd assured Vera it was safe to return to London. Vera and Hannah, together with Vera's husband, Jack, were the last close family she had left. She couldn't bear it if anything happened to them.

Jess supposed she must have comported herself well enough through the meal, because the other women were smiling at her as the last of the dessert dishes were cleared away and the group moved through to the anteroom to take their coffee. She made more of an effort to pay attention to the conversation and put her worries aside. As soon as she had enough free time she would go to the little house on Farthing Lane and tell Auntie Vera she had to return to Wales. And it was only a rumour, Jess reminded herself. There had been talk of Nazi death rays and mysterious weapons throughout the war, but apart from the flying bombs, rumour had always proved more alarming than the reality.

She was distracted from her dark thoughts when the woman Jess recognised as the president of the Messing Committee rose. 'I see we have two new officers who need to be formally introduced to the mess,' she said, speaking in a refined accent that must surely have been polished at a finishing school.

A murmur of approval greeted those words and a reluctant grin tugged at the corners of Jess's mouth. She knew what was coming. She and May were to be initiated through whatever ceremony had been devised by this particular mess. A bit of fun was exactly what she needed.

'What's going to happen?' she asked Evie.

Evie pointed at the ceiling. Jess looked and saw black footprints decorating the white paint of the ceiling between the beams. Each footprint was signed.

'How do they get up there?'

'You'll find out. Take off your shoes and stockings, both of you.'

Jess obeyed, seeing May do the same. When they stood in bare feet, the officer who had spoken first said, 'Bring the ashes.'

A more junior member of the mess dashed to the fireplace and returned with a tray of cold ashes, grinning broadly.

Beginning to understand, Jess dipped her right foot into the ashes, then suppressed a squeal as she found herself lifted upside down. She giggled as the blood rushed to her head, and she felt hairpins flying out. She clutched at her skirt. 'Wait, 'ave a care,' she cried. 'I don't want to go flashing my unmentionables to all and sundry.' Thank heavens she was wearing her more respectable knickers today and her racy French lace creations were safely folded in her suitcase, waiting to be unpacked. She giggled again as many hands rotated her until her feet pointed towards the ceiling. Angling her head so she could see where there was a clear white space, she pressed the sole of her foot onto the ceiling, leaving a slightly smudged black foot-print. Then the room spun around as the hands turned her the right way up and her feet met the polished floorboards. One of the waiting staff hurried forward with a bowl of water and a towel. As Jess washed the soot off her foot and dried it, she saw May plant her own footprint onto the ceiling. Finally they were handed pencils and climbed onto chairs to sign their names.

'There,' said Evie, handing Jess her hairpins, you're both officially inducted into the mess.

Jess and May tidied their hair and sank into armchairs in a quiet corner, joined by Evie. Soon the chatter and laughter from other officers died down as those on night watch drifted off to their rooms to get a couple of hours' sleep before they needed to leave. Others picked up books or letters and peace descended.

'What watches are you in?' Evie asked, glancing between Jess and May.

'A Watch,' both said simultaneously.

'Me too,' they both said again, then burst out laughing.

'Well, if that isn't the icing on the cake,' Evie said. 'That's my watch.' Then she paused and wrinkled her forehead. 'Unless… will that be too strange?'

'Are you joking?' Aware of the presence of some very senior officers, Jess resisted the urge to dance a pirouette. 'It's wonderful. We'll be off duty at the same time.'

May gave an emphatic nod. 'And I won't be nearly so nervous tomorrow with you looking out for us.' Evie squeezed May's arm. 'I'll always look out for you. Both of you.'

Jess was nothing but pleased for Evie; her friend had earned her position by sheer flair and hard work. 'We've got your back too. Never doubt it.'

–

'Did you say your aunt was back in London?' Evie asked Jess after a short silence. When Jess nodded, Evie went on, 'It would be lovely to meet her after all you've told us about her. And your cousin. What did you say her name was?'

Jess tensed. 'Hannah.' She didn't know why, but she'd never expected this. Never thought her friends might want to meet her family. She couldn't imagine why this hadn't occurred to her. She had visited Evie's home in Cowley a few times when she and Evie had managed to arrange forty-eight-hour passes at the same time. It was only natural that Evie would be curious to meet Jess's family now she had met Evie's mother. It was different for Evie, though. She had nothing to hide.

'Better let me see them alone the first time,' Jess said. 'Hannah's rather shy, so I wouldn't want her to be overwhelmed.'

'Nothing like you, then,' Evie said with a smile. Then, thankfully, she let the matter drop. 'Anyway, I've had some good news from Alex. Guess what?'

'Don't tell me, he's been made Air Vice Marshall.'

Evie punched Jess on the arm. 'Idiot. No, but he's been transferred to Intelligence.'

'So he's not doing operational flying?'

Evie nodded, beaming. 'It's such a relief not to have to worry about him every day. And he's based nearby.'

Jess raised an eyebrow, something she'd practised in front of a mirror for hours when she'd been an aspiring actress. 'Dare I suggest we might soon be hearing wedding bells?'

Evie's cheeks flushed. 'We haven't spoken of it.'

'It's only a matter of time. You mark my words.'

There was silence for a moment, and Jess picked up a newspaper. She found she couldn't focus on any of the articles as the news about Alex sank in. Her dreams of the three friends returning to the same comradeship they had known in Amberton seemed to be dying. Evie wouldn't be spending much time with her friends now Alex was within easy reach. And May would probably spend as much of her free time as possible with Peter.

Of course, Alex and Peter had both been at Amberton, but it hadn't seemed to matter so much. Not with Milan there.

Jess had done her best not to think of Milan in the years since she had left Amberton. Now, with all the talk of Alex and Peter, she found herself wondering where he was.

'Do you know what the other members of Brimstone are up to?' she asked, trying to sound casual.

'They were rotated to a quieter area for a while – somewhere up in Scotland. I only managed to see Alex once while they were up there.' Evie's lips twitched. 'And before you come up with some feeble excuse for asking after Milan, he's absolutely fine. Although he and Jiří were posted to RAF Benson.'

'Benson?' Jess couldn't hide her surprise. As far as she knew, RAF Benson was a reconnaissance base. 'What are they doing there?'

'Apparently they complained when they were sent to Scotland. Said they wanted to be on active duty, not kick their heels doing training flights in the Highlands. Next thing they knew, they were being transferred. At any rate—' Evie shot Jess a sly smile '—Benson's not too far away.'

Jess pulled out her compact and made a pretence of examining her hair. 'Can't think why I'd be interested. I haven't thought of Milan in years.'

'Then you won't mind if we run into him in London sometimes? He and Alex still meet.'

The compact slipped from Jess's fingers onto her lap. She managed to grab it before it fell to the floor. 'Doesn't bother me.' Jess smoothed a lock of hair behind her ear before closing the compact with a snap and replacing it in her pocket. She gave Evie a bright smile. 'Reconnaissance, eh? I doubt Milan's happy with that.'

Chapter Two

He was home, walking through his hometown. It was full summer, and the sun beat down on him, warming his back. This wasn't the feeble sunshine you got in England but the strong heat of a Czechoslovakian summer. It threw the terracotta tiles on all the roofs into sharp relief, the waves of each one marked by clear light and shade. The smell of resin from the sun-warmed pine trees beyond the buildings filled the air. Hens scratched the dry soil in the front yards he passed, their soft clucks mingling with the deep grunts of the few pigs to form the background noises of his childhood.

The road sloped downhill and soon he had left behind the small town and had turned onto the track leading into the woods. The track where his home lay. He strained to look ahead, seeking out his childhood house. The house where Eliška and Franta lived. Were they still there? He quickened his pace.

Neighbours called out to him as he passed: 'Milan – welcome home!'

He nodded to them and said a brief hello in return but didn't slow his pace. His heart sped up as he followed the track around the bend. There it was! The large, solidly built house with its white walls, deep-set windows and terracotta roof. Were they there?

He pushed open the gate, dry mouthed.

A high, piping voice called out. '*Strejdo Milane!*' Then Milan saw the tiny figure of his nephew running down the path, kicking up puffs of dust with each step. Eliška followed. Even from this distance Milan could see the tears running down her cheeks.

Milan dropped his case, grabbed Franta and swung him around, whooping and laughing. He was home, and everything was exactly as he remembered it. Nothing had changed. His fears had come to naught.

Franta was speaking again but a bell jangled in his ear, making it impossible to hear.

Milan opened his eyes and fumbled his arm free of the bed covers to turn off his alarm. Then he stared up at the ceiling, disoriented.

He would have thought by now that he would have got used to the dream, wouldn't experience the horrible lurch of realisation when it hit him that he wasn't home. He was in England, the war still raged, and he had not heard from his sister and nephew since the Nazis invaded and he had been forced to flee. He couldn't understand how he could dream the same dream night after night and awaken every time with a fleeting sense of lightness until reality crashed in.

Half an hour later, having been to the station Met Office to confirm the weather was suitable for flying and then eaten a light breakfast, he went to the Ops Room to check out what missions were on. While he studied the blackboard where the flying programme was listed, Jiří arrived.

'Nothing for me,' he said, sounding disgruntled.

Their flight commander chose that moment to arrive. 'Should have returned your Spitfire in one piece yesterday instead of full of holes,' he told Jiří. Then he turned to

Milan. 'You're doing a run to the Netherlands.' He handed Milan instructions on the target to be photographed.

'Sounds like a milk run,' Jiří said, once the flight commander had moved off.

'Should be. See you at lunch.' Milan gave Jiří a casual wave and headed outside to where the Humber Snipes were waiting to transport the pilots to the Intelligence Room for the briefing.

Concentrating on the briefing and then marking up his course on his chart, Milan was able to push his dream from his mind. However, once he was alone at the controls of his Spitfire, up in the air and watching the coast of Northern France coming into view, it all came back to him. He gazed east across the rolling landscape, straining his eyes until the horizon met the sky. That was the way to Czechoslovakia and home. Somewhere out there were his sister and young nephew. Pray God they were still alive. If only he could keep on flying, he would get there eventually.

A futile wish, of course. Even though his Spitfire was fitted with extra fuel tanks to give him the range, he would be shot out of the sky long before he got there. The modifications that transformed his Spitfire into a reconnaissance plane left no room for guns.

Yet again he marvelled at the irony that had brought this change of fortune. When he and Jiří had protested against being rotated to quieter duties, they had done so because they wanted to continue the fight. What on earth had possessed Fighter Command to decide some of their best pilots should be moved to reconnaissance? He didn't want to shoot pictures; he wanted to shoot Nazis. He wanted to kill and keep killing until he'd cleared a path for the Allied Advance all the way to Prague.

The Allies would be somewhere on the ground, far below. Not that he could see them from this height, but they would be there, strengthening their grip on the territory they had already taken back from the Nazis and chipping away at the retreating forces where they were trying to dig in. Too slow, though. They hadn't even succeeded in liberating Paris yet and they'd been in France since May. At this rate it would be months, maybe years before they reached Czechoslovakia.

Milan clenched his jaw. If only his Spitfire was carrying machine guns instead of cameras, he'd do his bit to oust the Nazis. But he didn't have so much as a pea-shooter.

A glance at the coastline and then the chart on his knees told him he was now over Belgium and therefore enemy territory. He forced himself to concentrate on the task at hand. Anyone who thought reconnaissance flying was a safe option needed their heads testing. If the Luftwaffe sent planes after him he had nothing with which to defend himself. All he'd be able to do was take some nice photos of the scenery as it came rushing up to meet him.

His collar chafed his neck as he turned his head to scan the skies. No sign of enemy aircraft, and the Spitfire wasn't leaving a vapour trail, so the blue plane would be difficult to see against the sky. He could only hope the Luftwaffe was too busy defending the German troops in Paris to bother about a single RAF plane making its way to the Belgium–Netherlands border. He consulted his chart again then looked at the ground, looking for the Scheldt. Once there, he needed to fly due east to the area of woodland he'd been sent to photograph. He gave a grunt of satisfaction when he spotted the ribbon of blue threading its way inland, and adjusted his course. Not long now and he should be at his target.

From his height of thirty thousand feet, the ground looked like a piece of green pottery, with roads and canals appearing like cracks in the glaze. As he studied the ground, he was aware of his hands growing uncomfortably cold. He warmed his hands against his neck in turn, wishing someone would invent a pair of gloves that didn't make his hands feel too clumsy to handle the aircraft.

Glancing at the ground again, he saw a patch of darker green, roughly trapezoidal in shape, and knew he'd reached his destination. He relaxed slightly. All he had to do now was take the photographs and head for home on a direct course. He banked until the target disappeared beneath the Spitfire's nose then straightened and turned the cameras on. This was the best way to capture the target, as the cameras were mounted behind the cockpit. Thankfully there was no cloud cover so once he was past the target he knew he would have taken clear images of the ground. It was strange to be taking photographs of woodland. He could see nothing but trees with just a single straight line cutting through them marking a road. At his briefing he'd been told it was a possible launch site for flying bombs, but he could see nothing to indicate anything suspicious. He ground his teeth. Here he was photographing trees when he should be fighting Nazis.

By this time he was past the target so he turned off the cameras and checked his compass, preparing to turn and plot his return course. It was as he banked that he saw them: three Messerschmitts maybe ten thousand feet below, climbing in his direction. Then a glance over his shoulder turned his heart to lead. He had been so occupied in photographing the target that he had neglected to check if he was leaving a vapour trail, and now a white ribbon stretched out behind, guiding the Messerschmitts straight to him. If they caught him up, he didn't stand a chance.

Although he had no weapons, he had one advantage: his Spitfire's greater manoeuvrability. If he could prevent the formation of a vapour trail, he would have the best chance of escape. Making sure he was on a course heading for the sea, he dived to lose height, continuously switching his gaze between the enemy planes and the treacherous trail. He could only pray he didn't have too much height to lose before the atmospherics were right to prevent formation of a contrail. The Messerschmitts came closer as he lost height. He held his breath, heart hammering. At last the white trail faded and petered out. Immediately he banked sharply, veering away from the fading contrail. Just as he did so, something struck his machine, and he knew he'd been hit. He could only pray the bullets had struck nothing vital. He changed direction again and again, all the while checking that his general course was bringing him closer to England. No further bullets struck, and after another series of course changes, he looked out to see the Messerschmitts were tiny dots far behind.

Milan slumped in his seat, the tension draining. They wouldn't catch him now. They certainly wouldn't chase him across the channel where they would be likely to run into RAF patrols.

It was only when he crossed the coastline that he thought to check his fuel gauge. It was low and sinking fast. The strike he'd felt must have holed his fuel tank. The question was, did he have enough fuel to get back to England?

Moments later the engine spluttered and died.

–

'Feels like the first day at school, doesn't it?' Jess said to May as they set off after breakfast with the other officers of A Watch. A heavy dew lay on the grass and the early morning sunlight lit the garden with a golden glow, shining on dew-beaded cobwebs that decked the towering runner beans on their canes. Despite it being only mid-August, there was an autumnal feel to the morning that intensified the back-to-school feeling.

May nodded. 'I just hope I don't do something stupid.'

'You'll be fine,' Evie told them. 'But any problems or questions, just ask me.'

They set off at a brisk pace down the road, passing several large houses behind high walls or hedges. 'You certainly see how the other half live around here,' Jess muttered. It was a far cry from the narrow, crowded streets where she had grown up. It was hard to believe they were in the same city.

Before long they arrived at an imposing red brick house set behind a high wall. Beyond it the road ran downhill, and for the first time Jess could see they were situated on top of a hill. Through gaps in trees and buildings, she could catch glimpses of London spread out below. She would have loved to walk further to get a better view, but the others turned through the gateway, showing their passes to the guard at the entrance. To Jess's surprise, however, they didn't enter the house – more a stately home, Jess thought, gazing up at it. Instead, they skirted the buildings, taking a path that led into extensive grounds.

'Blimey,' Jess said, taking in the gardens and trees and even a small pool twinkling in the sunlight, 'you could fit the whole of Poplar in here.'

'We're in the building across the lawn,' Evie said. 'There's a canteen up on the third floor in the main house.'

Jess looked back at the house. 'Looks like it would take most of your break time to get there.'

'It's no fun in the dark,' another girl told her. 'I'm always terrified I'll fall in the pond.'

'I thought we'd be in a bunker.' Jess wasn't sure how she felt about working somewhere that seemed unprotected against attack.

'The Filter Room used to be in a bunker up at Bentley Priory,' Evie answered. 'But I hadn't been there long when it was taken over. We found out later it was used for planning the Normandy landings. We got sent down here to Hill House.'

The guard at the entrance saluted them as they showed their passes. Jess's nerves returned as she put her pass away and followed Evie inside.

Shoulders back, chin up and smile, she recited in her head. It was one of the first things she had learnt as an actress and was the best way she had discovered to trick herself into feeling confident. She glanced at May and gave an approving nod when she saw her friend correct her own posture and raise her chin. The Christmas they had put on a pantomime felt a lifetime ago, but May had clearly remembered Jess's lessons.

The other Filterers, Evie included, went through the inner doors into what Jess knew must be the Filter Room. However, the Filter Officer, Flight Officer Laura Morgan, took Jess and May aside. 'Good. Neither of you look like you're dying of nerves. While I'll do what I can to support you, of course, we need Filterers who can work quickly and accurately with the minimum of direction. You might think Rudloe Manor and RAF Watnall were busy, but this is something else again.' She put a hand on the door then glanced back at the two friends. 'We stagger the changeover here to minimise disruption.'

Jess nodded. She was used to this from her previous posting.

'You two will change in last. Take the time to observe the Filterer you're relieving and familiarise yourself with the tracks and Chain Home stations in your area.'

May and Jess followed Morgan through the doors that led to the Filter Room. Immediately Jess was struck with the hum of noise. She was used to the chatter filling a Filter Room from her other posts – so different from the near silence she had worked in as an Operations Room plotter. The layout of the room was the same as the other Filter Rooms she knew, with the large map table showing the coast, divided into grids with coloured arcs radiating out from each Chain Home station. Above was the balcony occupied by the Controller, the Filter Officer, and the Movements Liaison Officer, who co-ordinated information on the movements of friendly aircraft. The Tellers, who reported the filtered information on to the Operations Room, and the Speed Orderly had their own corners.

By force of habit, Jess glanced at the pulse clock and colour code indicator as she took her place then studied the tracks on display, making note of the times each had been placed. The Filter Plotters were clustered around the table, speaking into their headsets. Each Filter Plotter was connected with one of the Chain Home stations displayed on the map, and communicated with that station's RDF operator. Whenever they received information of a new track from the RDF Operator, the Filter Plotter would place a counter on the map showing the position, then place numbers showing the range, height and estimated number of aircraft and also whether the track was 'friend or foe'. Jess, who had done a stint as an RDF operator herself, knew friendly aircraft carried a transponder that caused a 'double blip' to appear on the screen. The number of aircraft was estimated from the size of the dip the signal returned on the cathode ray tube the RDF operators viewed. It took skill and experience to estimate these numbers, and it was part of her duties as Filterer Officer to get to know the Chain Home Stations so she could assess the accuracy of their readings.

Of course, different Chain Home stations could receive signals from the same flight, meaning two tracks on the table might represent the same aircraft. It was the Filterer Officer's job to assess the tracks and decide if they showed the same information. If they did, the Filterer Officer combined them into a single track, placing a 'halma' – literally a plastic piece like those used in the game of Halma – for each individual track. She also had to make a judgement on the correct information to give for range, height and number of aircraft. This process was called filtering. It was vital to perform this quickly, as the information could not be passed on to the Operations Room – and thus sent out to the various sector stations around the country – until the information had been filtered.

Jess's nerves faded as she observed the table. It might be busier here and even more pressured, but she knew her job and she could handle it. She caught May's eye and saw the same relief in her expression. She gave an encouraging smile.

After that there was no more time to think. Laura Morgan directed her to take her place, relieving the

Filterer she'd been observing, and now Jess was in the thick of things. Thankful she'd had the time to get to grips with the situation, she quickly combined a track already on display with information that had been reported by the next RDF station along the chain. It had been identified as a friendly flight – probably a bomber raid returning from a mission. Soon other friendly aircraft were reported following the same course, confirming Jess's opinion that this was a returning bombing raid. She had tracked many such flights in her time and knew that although the bombers set out en masse, they tended to get spread out on return, depending on how much damage they had sustained during the raid. She knew to keep an especial eye on any stragglers, as they could be severely damaged and in danger of needing to ditch in the sea. If their signal disappeared, the relevant Operations Room would need accurate information of their last known position so help could be sent.

There was one such straggler Jess was concerned about, although it hadn't appeared from the same direction as the main flight of returning bombers. Instead it had been picked up just off the coast near the border between the Netherlands and Belgium. She was sure it was a single aircraft, and it emitted IFF identification, the signal that it was friendly. It was heading for the coast of East Anglia, but losing height. Jess felt a twinge of anxiety. In all likelihood, the aircraft had sustained damage.

'Ask Bawdsey for another reading on that track,' she said to the plotter.

'Yes, ma'am,' replied the plotter and spoke to the RDF Operator at Bawdsey over her headset. A moment later she moved the track a little closer to the English coast, but the altitude was another thousand feet lower.

'It looks like he's going to end up in the sea,' Jess said. 'Tell Bawdsey to keep an eye on it and let us know the instant they lose the signal.'

Although the table was busy, Jess managed to keep an eye on the straggler, knowing quick action could mean the difference between life and death to the pilot. It held out for much longer than she could have expected, making it to within a mile of the Essex coast before the signal was lost. This was the bit Jess hated. She had done her job and knew a rescue launch would even now be setting out towards the last known position of the ditched plane. The trouble was, she would probably never find out if the pilot had made it. Once the information had been sent to the relevant Operations Room, that was the end of her job. Nevertheless, she spared a thought for the unfortunate pilot whenever there was a lull in the action and hoped he had been found alive.

Chapter Three

There was little time to ponder the fate of the ditched pilot, however.

'Ma'am,' said one of Jess's plotters, 'the RDF operator has reported a Diver.'

There was no time to lose. 'Diver' was the code word for a flying bomb, otherwise known to the public as a doodlebug or buzz bomb.

'Diver, Diver, Diver,' Jess called, alerting the rest of the Filter Room even as she placed a halma. Seconds later the plotter placed a revised position, enabling Jess to see the course of the flying bomb. If it wasn't stopped at the coast, it would reach the heart of London.

All the time she was concentrating on the plotting table, she was aware of the Filter Officer watching the action from the balcony, assessing her performance. Working swiftly, she extrapolated the course and read out the co-ordinates of the point where the bomb would cross the coast. Jess knew one of the tellers would get on the line immediately to alert the nearest gunnery positions. The guns had been moved to the coast from London to tackle the flying bombs. Shooting them down over London would be just as dangerous as allowing the bombs to fall, as the flying bombs would explode where they fell. Their best hope was for the flying bombs to be shot down as they crossed the coast. If they got through, their only hope was for fighter aircraft to flip the bomb over so it was diverted out to sea. This was a difficult and dangerous manoeuvre.

Jess, mentally extrapolating the bomb's course, saw it could strike in the East End. She had a fleeting thought of her Auntie Vera and Hannah before pushing her fears for them to the back of her mind. She could best protect them by doing her job, and that meant not dwelling on her fear but concentrating solely on the tracks.

Even so, her mouth went dry as the track approached the coast and she waited for the plotter's next update.

'Still no signal, ma'am,' the plotter said with a shake of the head when Jess asked. A moment later the Observer Corps reported that the flying bomb had been destroyed.

'Nice work,' she said to the plotter.

That was all the celebration she was allowed, for moments later another 'Diver' report came through.

–

'That was relentless,' Jess said to May when A Watch came off duty and walked out into the sunny grounds of Hill House.

May nodded and flopped down onto the grass. 'I thought the Filter Room at Rudloe Manor was busy, but this was something else.'

When they had arrived that morning, Jess had been too focused on surviving her first day to take much notice of her surroundings, but now she could appreciate the location. 'I have to say, this makes up for the hard grind,' she said with a sweeping gesture that took in the gardens, the extensive lawn and lake. 'It's even better than High Chalk House.'

She lay back on the grass, allowing the sun to warm the muscles that were stiff from hours of intense concentration.

Footsteps approached, swishing through the grass. They stopped not far from Jess's head.

'That's pretty much how I felt after my first watch,' said a familiar voice. Jess squinted up at a face framed with red hair that glowed in the sunlight.

'I 'ope you don't expect me to salute, cos I'm too tired to budge,' Jess said to Evie.

Evie chuckled and sank onto the grass between Jess and May. 'I'll let you off just this once.'

'Is it always like this?' May asked, shifting to give Evie space to lie down.

'Oh no.' Evie took off her cap, shook out her hair and lay back with a sigh. 'Sometimes it's much busier.'

The three friends lay in companionable silence for a while. Jess gazed up into the sky, empty save for a few high white clouds. It was hard to believe the peaceful sight could be so deceptive, and a flying bomb could be crossing the Channel at this very moment and heading this way. Right now, though, she comforted herself that the only sounds she could hear were the whirr of grasshoppers and the chatter of the other off-duty WAAFs sunning themselves in the grounds.

Finally May broke the silence. 'How did we do?' she asked Evie. 'I have to say, I was so glad it was you keeping an eye on us. Laura Morgan seems nice, too. I would have been far more nervous if there had been an old dragon up on the balcony like the Filter Officer we had at Rudloe Manor.'

'You both did brilliantly,' Evie said. 'And I have to tell you that the old dragon at Rudloe Manor sent a glowing report. Don't worry. Neither of you would be here unless you'd already shown you worked to a high standard. I knew you'd do well.' Evie sat up, took off her tunic and brushed the grass from the back. 'Anyway, we're not on duty again until tomorrow afternoon. What would you like to do in the morning? I could show you around Stanmore. There are lovely walks around the common.'

May agreed, but Jess shook her head. 'I'd love to, but you'll have to take me another time. I need to visit Auntie Vera. I don't mind telling you the number of flying bombs we picked up were a real eye opener.'

'Jess,' Evie said, a note of warning in her voice.

'Oh, don't worry, I won't breathe a word of what I've seen in the Filter Room.' Jess sat up with a groan and brushed the grass from her own tunic. 'But the flying bombs are hardly a secret, and I won't be easy while I know Vera and Hannah are in the firing line. I wish I hadn't told them it was safe to come back.'

'Why don't we come with you?' Evie said. 'I know Hannah's shy, but are we really so terrifying? I'd love to meet her. And your aunt.'

Jess felt her expression freeze. Before she could respond, May chipped in. 'Me too. We'll be kind to Hannah. If anyone knows what it's like to be shy, it's me.'

Jess wished she hadn't used Hannah's timidity as an excuse. 'I know, but—'

Evie's eyes narrowed. 'Unless there's another reason?'

The warmth seemed to drain from the air, and a ringing in Jess's ears drowned the birdsong. She looked at Evie in dismay. Had she guessed?

Before Jess could think of a suitable reply, Evie went on, 'I know what it's like working with officers who come from rich backgrounds, but this is us, for goodness' sake. I

31

grew up in Cowley. I'm not going to look down my nose at you just because you come from the East End.'

Summer returned to the garden; the birds' twittering filled the air. Too overcome with her reprieve, she couldn't immediately refute Evie's suspicions, much as it pained her that Evie thought she was ashamed of her background.

'And my dad and older brother are in prison,' May said. 'If anyone's going to be looked down on, it'll be me.'

'You'll have to find me a chair first,' Jess said. Giddy with relief, she spoke without thinking. The moment the words were out of her mouth she wished she could take them back, knowing May was sensitive about her height. Her worry about her friends meeting Hannah had got her well and truly rattled. She was always chiding May for talking herself down, so doing it herself was unforgivable. 'Sorry, May.' She patted her friend on the arm. 'I'm just jealous. I'd give anything to be as tall and elegant as you.'

But May was laughing and waved away her apology. It warmed Jess's heart to see how May's confidence had grown in the years since they'd first met.

'Look,' she said, 'I'd love you to meet my aunt. I've told 'er all about you two. But it's ages since I last saw 'er, so I'd really like to spend some time with her alone first. Another time, eh?'

As her friends assured her they understood, the knot of tension that had formed in Jess's stomach unwound. With luck, she'd be able to persuade Vera to return to Wales with Hannah. Vera and Hannah would be safe and there would be no danger of her friends meeting Hannah.

She sprang to her feet. 'Now, we've got a whole evening off. What is there to do around here for a girl to let off steam?' She linked arms with Evie and May. 'After a wash and brush-up, the three of us are going to hit the town. You, Evie my girl, are going to show us where the RAF officers are to be found.'

–

Jess paused, about to knock on her aunt's door when high-pitched giggles from the street made her look round. Five children rounded the corner, three girls and two boys, their clothes torn and covered in grime. One girl held something cradled in her hands; the other children clustered around, examining it.

But it was another girl who made Jess's breath catch in her throat. Her blonde hair had been tied back in pigtails but one plait had unravelled and the other seemed to be so covered in dust, it looked more grey than blonde. Although Jess could only see her face in profile, she would have recognised her anywhere. Hannah.

Seeing her evoked a wave of longing that was a physical knot of pain in her stomach. She closed her eyes for a moment, fighting her urge to sweep the little girl into her arms. But their reunion could wait. She needed a serious word with Vera, and it would be easier without Hannah there. She tore away her gaze and rapped on the door.

'Jess, my girl!' Jess had hardly stepped through the door into her Auntie Vera's house when she was engulfed in a lily-of-the-valley scented hug. 'It's so good to see you.'

Jess returned the hug, surprised by the tears that pricked her eyelids. She hadn't seen Vera since a quick visit to the relative in Welshpool where she and Hannah had moved to escape the Blitz.

Vera stepped back. 'Now, let me take a look at you. Oh, don't you look fine in your uniform. Your mother would have been so proud.'

Jess had to take her word for it; she barely remembered her mother who had died of tuberculosis when Jess was only six. Vera and her husband, Jack, had taken her in and lavished so much love on her, Jess had never felt the lack of a mother. Her father had died in a dockyard accident before Jess had been born.

She looked her aunt up and down, reassuring herself she was well. 'You're looking good yourself, Auntie.' Vera's shiny blonde hair was arranged in perfect victory rolls and her smiling lips were coloured with her favourite deep rose lipstick. It was Vera who had taught Jess to take pride in her appearance. When she and Vera had gone out together before the war, not all the heads that turned were looking at Jess.

'Come in, come in. I'll make tea.' Vera moved towards the kitchen then paused. 'Hannah's out playing with her friends but I can call her in.'

She moved towards the door; Jess stopped her with a hand on her arm. 'I've already seen her. Leave her be.' She grinned. 'Besides, you'll want to scrub 'er down in the yard before you let 'er anywhere near your clean floors.'

Vera sighed. 'If she's been playing in the rubble again, I'll 'ave 'er guts for garters. Honestly, I don't know where she gets it from. I swear, she'll turn my hair snow white before long.'

Jess went to put the kettle onto the stove and eyed her aunt's hair critically. 'Get on with you. You 'ain't got a single grey 'air on your head.' Vera was only in her early forties and could pass for much younger.

Vera patted her hair, looking pleased. 'Tell me all about life in the WAAF. Are you on leave?' Vera frowned and looked past Jess into the narrow hallway. 'I don't see any case.'

'I'm not on leave. I've just got the morning off. I've been moved to London. Well, Stanmore. But it's only a tube ride away.'

'Fancy that. So you'll be able to visit more often.'

Jess nodded. She opened her mouth to reply but a shrill whistle from the kettle interrupted. She hastily spooned tea into the warmed pot and poured the boiling water over it.

'We'll take it into the front room,' Vera said. 'It's too dingy in the back room now the windows are boarded up.'

The front room was exactly how Jess remembered, with the same battered couch opposite the tiny fireplace and an armchair on either side. The walls were covered with picture frames containing Uncle Jack's beloved cigarette card collection.

No sooner had Vera poured the tea than Jess broached the subject that had brought her to Poplar. 'I wish you would go back to Wales, Auntie. London's still not safe.'

'It's a sight safer than it was in the Blitz, and the house survived in one piece. Anyway, you're the one who said London was safe.'

'I know, but I forgot about the flying bombs. It would only take one.' Jess wished she could tell Vera what Evie had said about a new weapon. It would make this so much easier.

Vera stirred her tea. There was no sugar, so it was either out of habit or simply to buy her time to frame her next words. 'There's nothing for us in Wales. None of the kids would be friends with poor Hannah. They teased her something rotten for her accent and said she was a dirty slum child. Although how they had the cheek to say that when Hannah was the best turned-out child in Welshpool, I don't know.'

Jess put down the slice of fruit cake she'd been holding, her appetite suddenly gone. 'You never said so before.'

'I didn't want to worry you. There was nothing you could have done, and you were right. While the Blitz was going on it was madness to stay in London when we had somewhere safe to go.'

'Was it really that bad?' It was at Jess's urging that Vera had taken Hannah out of London at the start of the Blitz. Jess, then working in the Operations Room of a fighter station near the Sussex coast, had known only too well how many bombers were swarming towards London every night, because she was plotting their progress. She had been sick with worry on Vera and Hannah's behalf.

Vera patted Jess's hand. 'Not at first. Hannah was just a tiny mite, happy to play in the garden, and there was plenty for me to do with the WVS. But she's five now, and she needs friends.'

'She needs to be alive and well more,' Jess said. 'The Allies are in France now. It can only be a matter of time until the end of the war.'

Vera snorted. 'It'll all be over by Christmas? These things always take longer than expected. How long is Hannah to be lonely? The longer she goes without friends, the harder it will be for her to make them when she gets back. And she was being bullied, Jess. I had to take her away.'

'But what about—?' Jess stopped when the front door slammed, and footsteps pattered up the passage.

'Mummy, can I—? Oh.' Hannah appeared in the doorway. Jess could only imagine she'd been rolling in the gutter since Jess had last seen her, because both plaits were now unravelled and her dress was so splodged with dirt, it was hard to tell what colour it was supposed to be.

Hannah gave a beaming smile and skipped into the room. 'Jess! I didn't know you were coming.'

Jess had to press her lips together to suppress their sudden trembling. Only when she was sure she could speak without her voice wobbling did she clear her throat and say, 'Hello, love. I'm so happy to see you.'

Hannah ran towards Jess who would have hugged her despite her mess, but Vera sprang to her feet, hands on hips. 'Hannah Louise Knight, don't you dare take a step closer until you've had a wash and changed your clothes. Do you want your cousin to think you're no better than a monkey in a zoo?'

'All right.' Hannah backed away then said in her high, clear voice, 'You'll still be here when I get back?'

When Jess nodded, Hannah beamed then sped off.

'Honestly, that child.' Vera shook her head but Jess could tell from the indulgent smile that Hannah wouldn't get into much trouble. 'I keep warning her not to wander into the bomb sites, but will she listen?'

'There won't be any bomb sites in Welshpool.'

'Now don't you start that again. We're staying here and that's final.'

'I—'

'I said that's final. Hannah was unhappy there and so was I. I missed Jack terribly.'

Jess knew when she was defeated. 'How is Uncle Jack?'

'Doing very well, although he's working all hours. Still, I mustn't complain. At least he's here and not in the forces.'

'Auntie Vera,' Jess said, speaking quickly before Hannah came back into the room. 'You know my two friends, Evie and May?'

'Oh, yes. Your letters are full of them. How are they?'

'Very well. They're in Stanmore too.'

'Then you must bring them here. I'd love to meet them.'

'I will, but—' Jess glanced through the doorway but there was no sign of Hannah. She must either be washing in the kitchen or getting changed. 'They don't know about… well, you know.'

Auntie Vera shot her a dark look. 'And you worry they'd think less of you if they found out? If they're half the friends you say they are, it shouldn't make any difference to them.'

'Maybe. I just… I couldn't bear to lose them.'

At the sound of running feet down the passage, Jess turned pleading eyes onto Vera.

'Don't worry. I won't say a word.'

A moment later, Hannah was running into the room, hands and face pink and shining as though they'd never been near dirt and wearing a clean gingham dress. 'Jess! Did you bring me a present?'

'Yes, I— *oof*!' This last exclamation was wrenched from her as Hannah hurled herself into Jess's lap. 'You're getting too big to do that.'

And the rest of the morning passed in laughter, present-giving and a loud and enthusiastic game of cards.

'Let me know when you're going to bring your friends. I've been saving my rations for your next visit so I can bake us a nice cake.' This was Vera's parting remark as Jess left after an early lunch.

'I will.' And Jess set off at a brisk walk for Bromley station, easier in her mind. She could bring Evie and May for a visit without fear of losing their friendship.

Chapter Four

Jess and May emerged from their first night watch, blinking in the sunlight.

'It's like coming out of the cinema,' Jess said, yawning. 'I'm always surprised when it's light outside.'

'And we've got a whole day to ourselves to enjoy it,' May said.

Jess's stomach chose that moment to give a loud gurgle. 'I don't know about you, but I'm going to the mess to get breakfast. Then I'm going to put my head down for a couple of hours or I'll never make it through to tonight. We're having a night on the town, remember.'

It had been, Jess decided later that evening as she walked with May and Evie to Stanmore tube station, the perfect day. After a leisurely breakfast followed by a restorative sleep, they had walked to the Spring Ponds for a swim. These were on private land, but the landowner had kindly allowed the members of No. 2 WAAF Officers' Mess to swim there. They were reached by a short walk across fields. After an energetic swim in the chill water that involved much splashing and giggling, they had climbed out to lie on their towels and dry in the sun. Now Jess was refreshed and looking forward to a night in the bright lights of London. Well, maybe not the bright lights – not with the blackout. Still, even after nearly five years of war, there was no thrill quite like a night in London, and she had been looking forward to this ever since she'd heard of her transfer.

'Alex is meeting us at Piccadilly Circus,' Evie said as they descended the steps to the platform.

'I wouldn't think you two need any help from Eros,' Jess said with a grin, referring to the famous statue.

But when they arrived, Jess saw that the statue had been dismantled and the plinth and basin were covered in boards. There was nothing to admire but a few peeling posters urging Londoners to invest in war savings. 'Good thing you don't need Eros's help,' she said sadly. Then again, Eros hadn't exactly led her to choose wisely when she'd been a naive actress, so maybe it was a good thing he had been packed away.

Then a figure emerged from the other side of the boarded-up plinth and Evie gave a cry of delight and flung herself into his arms. Jess and May turned away and made a show of talking among themselves. May dabbed at her eyes.

'Missing Peter?' Jess asked. She patted May's arm in a show of sympathy.

May nodded. 'I got a letter from him today, though, so I know he's all right. He's not too far from London, so we'll be able to meet fairly often.'

'I thought I heard his squadron had been posted overseas?'

'They have, but the RAF won't post him abroad because of his leg.'

'Of course.' Jess had forgotten Peter had a prosthetic leg. 'Where is he now?'

'Up in Suffolk. Carrying on with the work he was doing in Oldbourne.'

Jess nodded in understanding. Peter had been trialling airborne interception systems to aid in catching enemy bombers at night. Thanks to the work of pilots like him, it was becoming easier for pilots to navigate at night and find airborne targets.

They turned when Evie ran up behind them and grabbed their arms. 'Come on. Alex is taking us to a club he knows.'

All the evidence of her friends' happy relationships had made Jess feel lonely. She forced a smile. 'What are we waiting for? I for one am planning on dancing the night away with as many officers as I can find.'

But when they walked through the door of the Crescent Moon club, the soft notes of 'Moonlight Serenade' drifting into the night air, it was one officer in particular that made Jess stop dead.

Evie, who had been a few steps behind, her attention on Alex, bumped into Jess's back. 'Why have you stopped?'

Jess couldn't answer. All she could do was gaze at the man seated at a table near the stage. A strange roaring in her ears blotted out the music and her vision faded so that the dark-haired man was the only thing in focus. He wasn't looking her way but studying a menu card. Even though his head was lowered, she could see enough of his features to recognise the man who had set her heart aflutter while at Amberton. The man who had brought her heart to life when she had thought it had died for ever. The only man who had made her feel that way since—

Evie shook her arm. 'What's wrong?'

'Milan.' Saying the name seemed to break the spell; she could hear the music again and her vision returned to normal.

'Oh. Are you going to be all right?'

'Course I am. Me and Milan were never serious.'

Alex, who had entered last, caught them up and saw where they were looking. 'I bumped into Milan earlier today. He was at a bit of a loose end so I invited him to join us. I didna think you'd mind.'

'Why should I?' *Shoulders back, chin up and smile. No. Don't just smile – sparkle.*

Milan looked up from the menu and saw Alex approach, three women in WAAF uniform following. He recognised Evie straight away; he rose and greeted her then turned to her friends. His heart stuttered when he saw who they were. May stood in front of Jess, so he drew a breath and greeted her first. She could have replied in fluent Cantonese for all he knew; his whole attention was on Jess. He couldn't drag his gaze from her. Then before he knew it, May, Evie and Alex sat down, leaving him staring at the woman who had broken his heart. She had taken off her cap, and her hair gleamed gold in the light of the chandeliers.

'Nice to see you again, Milan,' Jess said. She gave him the same beaming smile that had dazzled him the first time they had met and every time after that. However awkward he felt at meeting her again, it was clear she had no such feelings. She met his gaze without flinching and carried herself with a confident posture that made her seem a good few inches taller than her actual height. What was she waiting for? Oh, yes. A reply.

'It is good to see you, too, Jess.' And it was. No matter how he had tried to forget her in the years since Jess had left Amberton, the memory of her was a song that he could never clear from his head.

Jess arched a perfectly shaped eyebrow, and he stared back uncomprehendingly. Then it struck him that he was standing between her and the table. She couldn't sit until he moved. The only remaining seat beside his own was the chair between him and Evie. Without knowing how he was going to cope spending the whole evening sitting so close to her, he pulled back the chair so she could sit. Then he took his seat.

Perhaps May had noticed the awkwardness, for she spoke at once. 'It's lovely to see you again, Milan. Evie mentioned you were on reconnaissance duties now.'

Milan grasped at the conversation opener eagerly. 'That is correct. Although I was forced to ditch my machine in the sea two days ago. I have to wait for another one.' Thankfully he had managed to recover the precious film without it getting damaged, although his CO had given him what one of the British pilots had described as 'a right royal dressing down' for losing the Spitfire.

'Two days ago?' Jess, who had been studying her drinks menu with unconvincing concentration spoke sharply. When Milan nodded, she laughed. 'Well, of all the—' she broke off then said. 'You know we can't speak of our work?'

'Of course.' He'd asked to be allowed to observe in Ops once when he'd been rotated to non-combat duties, so had a rough idea of what Jess did and knew the 'special duties' WAAFs were bound by in accordance with the Official Secrets Act.

'Well,' Jess said, 'let's just say that someone was watching over you that day.'

43

'Then thank you.' He understood then that Jess must have been involved in the chain of information that had sent the rescue launch to the right spot. 'If there had been any delay I don't think I could have held on.' His plane had been rapidly swamped in the choppy sea and the launch had arrived just in time.

Something in Jess's expression seemed to shift. She gave him an unreadable look. 'I'm very glad they picked you up. We never normally hear, you know. We just do our jobs and pray the people who need help get it.'

After all this time she still cared for him. The realisation gave him hope. He had been hurt and confused when Jess had ended their relationship. Other people had managed to keep relationships going while separated – it must be more unusual for couples to be living near each other with the war on. When Jess had insisted being with him had just been a bit of fun, it had thrown him. While he had always known she enjoyed flirting with the other pilots, he had been sure she had genuine feelings for him. There had been a softness in her face, an extra glow in her eyes when she had been with him that had never been there when she'd spoken to other men.

Come to think of it, though, there had been times she had deflected his questions when he'd asked about her acting jobs or her family. When that happened, her affection had always cooled for a day or two before she had shaken off whatever had bothered her and she'd returned to her usual bedazzling ways. At the time he'd excused her odd behaviour as a symptom of the stress they had all been under, struggling through the Battle of Britain and the early days of the Blitz. It was only now that the connection between his questions and her cooling off fell into place. She was hiding something, and he wished he knew what it was. He was sure nothing would make him feel any differently about her. Whatever secret she was hiding, it wouldn't change the fact that beneath her fun-loving, slightly vain exterior, she was loyal, intelligent, brave and caring.

The waitress arrived to take their orders.

'I will pay,' he said to the others. 'To celebrate my initiation into the Goldfish Club.' He tapped the flap of his left-hand pocket now holding a winged goldfish badge on its underside. It proved he belonged to the exclusive club of airmen who had survived a ditching at sea. 'And as thanks for my life,' he added, addressing Jess in particular.

When the waitress left, he wanted to speak more to Jess, but she was now in conversation with Evie.

'Do you still see the other members of Brimstone?' May asked, preventing him from joining the conversation with Jess and Evie. 'What is Jiří doing?' She faltered. 'He isn't…?'

'Jiří is fine,' he told her. He smiled. 'A little older but no wiser.'

'Thank heavens for that,' Jess said. May's mention of Jiří had caught the attention of all at the table. 'The day Jiří learns sense will be a sad day for all of us. I always laugh when I remember the two of you as the Ugly Sisters.'

'Or when he fell off the stage when he was in the pantomime stag costume,' May added, her eyes bright.

Amid the laughter that followed, Milan turned to Jess. 'So you do still think of me. That makes me glad.'

And as he went on to explain to May that Jiří was doing the same work as him, he couldn't help but notice how, although Jess had turned back to Evie, every now and then she would cast a glance in his direction when she thought he wasn't looking.

Much as he tried to focus on his conversation with May, he couldn't help overhearing what Evie was saying to Jess.

'Now you've been to visit your aunt alone, I would love to meet her and your cousin,' Evie said. 'And you can forget those crazy notions about us sneering at where you come from.'

So Jess was embarrassed about her background. Was that all it was – she thought she wasn't good enough for him? But that didn't strike true somehow. It was more likely to be a secret she was hiding, something about her past. Well, he wasn't going to give up. He would find out what it was then prove to her it didn't matter.

–

Jess's attempt to ignore Milan and talk to Evie was spoiled by Alex asking Evie to dance. He led Evie onto the dance floor, leaving just Jess, May and Milan. At least she had an excuse to turn Milan down if he asked her: it would be rude to leave May alone at the table. But then a young RAF officer with wings on his sleeve approached May.

'Excuse me,' he said, 'are you May Lidford? I think I've seen you with my CO, Peter Travis.'

'Oh, yes, I am,' May said.

'He'd tear off a strip if he knew I'd neglected you,' the young man said. 'Would you care to dance?'

Stammering her assent, May rose and allowed the officer to escort her onto the dance floor. Soon they were swaying in a respectable arm's length hold to the strains of 'I'll Be Seeing You'.

Milan turned to her, a glint in his eye. 'Remind me to buy that man a drink.'

'Why, was he part of your rescue team as well?'

'No. As you well know, I meant that I was grateful to him for leaving us alone.' Milan gestured towards the others. 'Would you like to dance?'

More than he would ever know. But that would involve being in Milan's arms, and Jess already knew how that felt, and knew she would find it hard to resist his advances if they got that close. 'I'd prefer to sit this one out if you don't mind.'

'I don't mind at all. It will be easier to talk sat here.'

She gave a little laugh and shook her head. 'I've got to hand it to you, Milan, you don't give up easily.'

Milan leaned across the table and fixed her with his gaze. 'Is that why you are alone – all the other men gave up too easily?' Then his expression changed. 'You *are* alone?'

'Yes, I'm alone. Why tie myself down to one man when I can have my pick?' She raised her glass and took a sip to hide her confusion. She had never met a man who could tie her in knots like this. Why hadn't she lied and told him she was with someone? Even as the thought crossed her mind, she knew she could never have done that. She had lied to him years ago when she'd told him she didn't care enough to carry on seeing him. That lie still haunted her. She didn't want to lie to him again.

'Yet none of the men you've picked are here with you tonight.'

Damn and blast him, why wouldn't he give up? 'It was supposed to be a night out with the girls, but Evie hadn't seen Alex in a while, so…' She waved her hand to indicate the couple entwined on the dance floor, Evie's head tucked into the crook of Alex's neck. She couldn't deny a twinge of melancholy at the sight. She was sure if Peter had been able to come tonight, he would be on the dance floor in much the same hold with May. Her happiness at finally being in the same place as her friends faded. Was this how it would always be, her being dropped whenever a friend's boyfriend was around? She couldn't blame them – in wartime you had to snatch whatever precious moments you could take with a loved one. Yet she couldn't deny it hurt to be left out.

The band reached the end of the song and the couples drifted back towards their tables. Milan leaned closer and spoke in an urgent voice. 'I do not want to play games, Jess. I would like to see you again. Thank you properly for your help.'

'You already have. I was doing my job. I don't expect thanks.'

'But I would like to offer it all the same. If you say no I won't bother you, but I want to keep seeing you, even if it is only as friends.'

She should say no. It was safer that way. She could keep other men at a distance, but Milan… she had missed him ever since their goodbye at Amberton, and she didn't know if she would have the strength to say goodbye to him again.

Evie, May and Alex returned to the table flushed and laughing. Milan moved away from Jess slightly but even when Jess smiled a greeting at her friends she was aware of his gaze fixed upon her.

'You'll never guess,' May said. 'Stewart – that's the officer I was dancing with – says Peter just got transferred to Uxbridge. That's not far. He found out today. Won't that be wonderful?'

Jess was happy for May, she truly was. 'That's marvellous. This is getting like the old times back at Amberton. We'll all have to go out together when he arrives.' She turned to Milan. 'You must come too,' she said. She slipped her arm through his. 'It will be wonderful to be all together again.'

Milan held her gaze, his piercing blue eyes seeming to see through to her soul. 'I will enjoy that,' he said. And she knew he didn't mean seeing the others. Was she being unfair? But surely it wouldn't do any harm to invite him to join the group. He had been an important part of life at Amberton, after all. And that way, she wouldn't be playing gooseberry.

Chapter Five

Jess looked in the mirror in the bedroom she shared with May as she pinned her hair up into gleaming rolls. She hadn't felt this jittery before a date since... well, since the last time she had gone out with Milan. Not that this was a date, she told herself. It was a reunion of old friends from Amberton. It would have been unthinkable to leave him out.

The bedroom door opened and May dashed in wearing her dressing gown, damp hair dangling in tendrils around her face.

Jess glanced at her watch. 'Get a move on or you'll be late.'

'I fell asleep in the bath.' May grabbed a comb and inspected her hair in the mirror. 'I'll have to catch you up.'

Jess arrived downstairs to see Evie putting down the phone. 'May's running late. She'll catch us up.' Another glance at her watch told her that the men would already be waiting for them.

'That was Alex,' Evie said, pointing to the phone. 'He's been held up and is just setting out. Why don't you go and meet Peter and Milan, and I'll wait for May.'

It was a sensible suggestion; they both knew how May would hate to walk into the pub alone. All the same, Jess couldn't help suspecting she was being set up.

That suspicion hardened when she walked into the Abercorn Arms on Stanmore Hill to see Milan alone at the bar. 'No sign of Peter?' she said, taking her place beside him. The Abercorn Arms – or simply the Abercorn, as it was known locally – seemed to have been taken over by the inhabitants of Bentley Priory for the duration. Nearly everyone present was in uniform, giving the impression that the décor was predominantly blue. Even the walls hadn't escaped, being covered in cartoons of one Pilot Officer Prune, a round-nosed character whose escapades demonstrated how not to survive various incidents.

Milan shrugged. 'He is not here.'

Against her better judgement, she couldn't help enjoying time alone with Milan again. Milan bought her a drink and they moved to a large corner table where they could keep an eye on the door. Jess took a sip of her port and lemon then gave Milan the benefit of one of her brightest smiles. 'Shall we take a bet on who will arrive last? We'll have to decide on a suitable prize for the winner.' Without thinking she had slipped into her role as incorrigible flirt, and the look she shot Milan hinted strongly at what kind of prize she was offering.

Milan set his beer glass down with a thump. 'Do not do that, Jess.'

'What am I doing?'

She expected him to say he didn't like her flirting; instead, he seemed to grope for words, sketching spirals in the air with his hands. 'You are like Ivy,' he said finally.

'What?' she felt an unexpected stab of jealousy. 'Who's she?' Had Milan been seeing a girl behind her back? Well, not behind her back, of course. She had finished with him, after all, so she shouldn't be surprised he had met someone else.

Now it was Milan's turn to look confused. 'Not a woman. A plant. You know. It grows around trees.' He made the spiralling gestures again, and now Jess understood that he was trying to demonstrate ivy twining around a tree trunk. She wasn't sure it was a flattering comparison. Ivy clung to living things and choked the life out of them.

'Well, you are a charmer,' she said with a laugh. 'So you think I'm a clingy weed?'

Milan shook his head, and a suspicion of a smile tugged at the corner of his mouth. 'That is not what I mean. Ivy covers a tree until it hides what lies beneath. It looks like a tree. But the ivy is not the tree.' He gave an exclamation of annoyance. 'It is hard to explain in English. But you are not the ivy, you are the tree. Most people see the ivy and say, "What pretty leaves," and don't try to see past them. But sometimes when I was with you, you let your guard down and I saw the tree, the real you, and that is the woman I like and admire. Why do you pretend to be the ivy?'

Her eyes smarted with unexpected tears. Milan might have stumbled over his explanation, but she knew exactly what he meant. There were very few people in her life she could be herself with. Her Auntie Vera and Uncle Jack were the only two who knew everything about her. She could be herself around Evie and May, but there were things even they didn't know. Yet here was Milan, whom she had rarely been alone with, telling her all about herself. She took a sip of port and lemon to clear the lump from her throat and buy herself time to come up with a suitable reply.

'I'm so sorry I'm late.'

Jess looked around with a start to see Peter Travis. How had he managed to get to the table without either of them noticing? 'Hello Peter,' she said, grateful for the interruption. All the while she was aware that Milan's gaze hadn't shifted from her. 'The others are running late, as you can see, but I'm sure they'll be here soon.'

Peter, however, glanced from her to Milan, looking uncomfortable. 'I hope I'm not interrupting anything.'

'Course not,' Jess said. 'It's good to see you. May was so excited when she heard you were moving to Uxbridge.'

Peter smiled, then shot Milan another look. 'Well, I'd better get a drink.' He made his way to the bar, the slight unevenness in his gait indicating his prosthetic leg was causing him discomfort.

He wasn't the only uncomfortable one. Jess knew she couldn't ignore Milan's observation. With anyone else she would have deflected him with a remark about not feeling much like a tree, but Milan had already shown he wouldn't accept anything other than words from the heart.

'It is all right,' Milan told her. 'You did not deny it, and that is all that matters.' His fingers were curled around his glass, and Jess noticed they tapped out an odd rhythm.

He followed her gaze. With a crooked smile he let go of the glass and placed his hand on the table, curling it into a loose fist. 'Playing the violin,' he said. 'My fingers do not forget, even though I have not picked up a violin since I fled Czechoslovakia.'

'You were a violinist?' It hadn't occurred to Jess to wonder what Milan had done before the Germans invaded his homeland. 'I thought you were always a pilot.'

'I was in my last year at university when it became clear the Nazis wanted Czechoslovakia. I could not let that happen so I joined the Czechoslovak Air Force. But I had always dreamed of being a concert violinist.' He grimaced. 'When the Germans came I had only one chance to take my plane and escape to Poland. There was no time to go back for my violin.'

'What of your family? Was there no time even to say goodbye?'

Only then did Milan look away. He studied the picture on his beer mat. 'There was just my sister and nephew by then. I had to leave without seeing them. I do not know if they are still alive.'

Jess gazed at him in horror. She could think of no adequate words to express her sympathy. All those months at Amberton, living side by side with the Czech pilots, they had been known for their high spirits. Now she could see those high spirits masked the grief of leaving behind their loved ones and their hopes and dreams.

She spoke without thinking. 'Is that why you could see through me so easily?' She hadn't meant to give herself away, but now she'd said the words, she was glad. Milan had revealed his true self; the least she could offer in return was an acknowledgement that he had read her correctly.

Milan gave a wry smile. 'When you have to show a different face every day to cover how you feel, you get to spot when others do the same.'

The door to the outside opened, and May, Evie and Alex burst in.

'I'm sorry we were so long,' Evie called as she flung her gas mask upon a chair and sat down beside Jess.

There was no more chance for Jess and Milan to speak alone, but she felt she had got to know more about him in those few minutes than in all the months she had known him in Amberton.

54.

When they rose to leave, Milan put a hand on her arm, preventing her from following the others outside. It was the first time they had touched since she had left Amberton all those years ago, and Jess shivered at the feel of his long, strong fingers through the sleeve of her tunic.

'Will you come out with me again?' Milan asked. 'Alone, I mean.'

'Yes.' The reply sprang to her lips without the need for thought.

When he beamed with pure happiness, she felt a twinge of guilt. She had no future with Milan, no future with any man. Her past actions had put paid to that. She had ended their relationship before because she hadn't wanted to lead Milan on only to let him down. On the other hand, his dream was to find his sister and become a concert violinist in Prague. There was no place for her in that life – she had no desire to leave England – so what was wrong in two lonely hearts finding solace together until the war was over? She couldn't let this be the last time she saw him, and after all they had shared, she knew if she turned him down now, she would never see him again. By the time they rejoined the others, he had arranged to call her as soon as he knew when he had another free evening.

–

'This is the life.' Jess lay back on her towel and stretched her arms above her head, enjoying the warm sunshine on her face. It was the last day of August, and the three girls were making the most of their day of leisure before going on the night watch. They had put on bathing suits under their clothes and walked across the fields to the Spring Ponds. The hedgerows were heavy with rosehips and dark, shiny blackberries, signs of the approaching autumn and a reminder that there may not be many warm days left to enjoy the ponds. They had splashed in the cool water for some time, giggling like schoolgirls. Now they had climbed out to lie on the sun-warmed bank and dry off. Jess could feel the tension of her last gruelling watch drift away.

'I hope we can come out here again before it gets too cold,' May said. 'This is the best way to unwind.'

'Other than going dancing with a certain red-haired squadron leader, you mean,' Jess said, giving May a nudge with her elbow.

'You can talk,' May retorted without rancour. 'I seem to recall you coming back late a few nights ago with stars in your eyes.'

'Just doing my bit to keep up morale among our brave pilots.'

'One brave pilot in particular.' Evie raised herself onto one elbow and gazed at Jess, shading her eyes. She had moved into the shade of a nearby tree to protect her fair skin from burning, and the dappled shadows quivered upon her bare arms with the light breeze that whispered in the leaves. 'I don't know if it's my imagination, but you don't seem to flirt with the men nearly as much as you used to.'

Jess had been out twice with Milan since meeting him at the Abercorn. While on both occasions they had done nothing but dine and talk, she couldn't think of a date she had enjoyed more. Thinking about it now wrapped her in a cocoon of happiness. 'Maybe I've grown up.'

'Maybe you've got deeper feelings for Milan than you're letting on.'

'I—' It was on the tip of her tongue to dismiss Evie's assertion with a quip, but Jess couldn't lie to her friends. 'So what if I have?'

Evie sat bolt upright. 'Oh my goodness. I was only joking. Do you really mean that?'

'Why? Do you think it's a bad idea?' Suddenly Jess was anxious, which was ridiculous – she never worried what her friends thought when she had seen other men.

'Of course not, you goose. It's marvellous, isn't it, May?'

May had also sat up, and now Jess could see she was grinning. 'It really is. I was so sorry when you two broke up. It was obvious to anyone with eyes how he felt about you.'

Jess did her best to ignore the twinge of guilt at the reminder, and she couldn't deny the flutter of pleasure she felt at May's confidence in Milan's regard for her. 'I thought you'd lecture me – warn me not to hurt his feelings,' Jess said, addressing this remark more to Evie than May.

Evie shook her head, giving Jess what she could only describe as a pitying look. 'Jess, you're not the heart-breaker you make out to be. You might be an incorrigible flirt, but I've never known you lead a man on. I'll confess to being a little concerned when you seemed to be seeing Milan at Amberton because I thought he was more serious than you. But you've obviously cleared that up with him.'

'I always thought you felt more for Milan than you were letting on,' May said.

'You did?' Jess was surprised. She had always thought she'd hidden her feelings so well.

'Oh yes. I used to catch you looking at him when you thought no one was watching. I could see from the

57

look in your eyes how you felt about him. I never really understood why you stopped seeing him.'

She would if she knew the truth. Jess hesitated. Should she confess? Was there a chance Evie and May would understand?

Evie pulled a comb from her bundle of clothes and started to work it through her tangled hair. 'Just tell me if I *do* need to give you a lecture. You know, like the one you gave me when I started to get serious about Alex.'

'No need to worry about that,' Jess said with a laugh. Good thing she hadn't confessed. She'd forgotten her concerned talk with Evie all those years ago, when she'd told Evie sternly to be careful and not let Alex pressure her into anything she wasn't ready for. Evie's shocked insistence she would never consider such a thing now came clearly to mind. No. Jess couldn't risk losing her friends' regard.

'Speaking of Alex,' Jess said, doing her best to deflect the conversation, 'how are things with the two of you now he's not on operational flying?'

Evie positively glowed, and not just because her face was in the sunlight. 'It's wonderful to have him nearby. In fact—' she lowered her voice even though there wasn't another soul in sight '—can you two keep a secret?'

As one, Jess and May moved closer.

'You can trust us,' Jess said, and May nodded her agreement, her face alight with curiosity.

'We've even talked about getting married.'

'Seriously?' Jess couldn't keep the shock from her voice although when she thought about it, she knew she shouldn't be surprised. Evie had been with Alex for four years. That was practically a lifetime in these dangerous times. They all knew couples who had married after only a few weeks' acquaintance. It was just the way things worked when couples didn't know if they would live to see each other again.

'Oh, we haven't made any definite decision yet, but what would you think if we decided to marry?'

'We'd be so happy for you,' May said. 'Wouldn't we, Jess?'

'Oh. Yes. That's right.' This was more to convince herself than Evie. What was wrong with her?

'It wouldn't change anything, you know.' Evie, bless her, must have sensed Jess's hesitation and discerned some of the feelings behind it. 'Alex has his work and I have mine. We won't see any more of each other than I do now. It's just—' Evie winced as her comb struck a stubborn tangle. 'Now the war is going our way at last, and it seems to be only a matter of time before we win, I want us to be together. For all we know, Alex could be posted overseas in another few months, so now seems like a good time to take the plunge.'

Jess gave Evie her best smile. 'As long as he makes you happy then you should do it. 'Ow long before we 'ave to call you Section Officer Kincaith?'

'Oh, goodness, nothing's definite yet. Promise you won't breathe a word. I just wanted to see what you thought.'

'Well, we're right behind you.' There were times when Jess was grateful for her experience as an actress. Then she turned wistful. 'So now you have your future all sorted. Marriage, kids, a little cottage with roses in the garden…'

Evie snorted. 'There's no way I'm settling down just yet, and Alex knows it. I'm not leaving the WAAF until after the war, anyway. We do important work.'

'And after?'

'I still want to do my maths degree.'

Jess hugged her knees. 'It must be nice to have an idea what you'll be doing after the war.'

'Won't you go back to acting?'

'Maybe. I don't know.' Jess picked at the grass. She didn't want to think too hard about her lack of prospects so nudged May with her foot. 'What about you? Will you be happy being Peter's wife or do you want a career too?'

A dreamy smile spread over May's face. 'I'll be more than happy being Peter's wife. Doesn't mean I don't want to do anything else, though.'

'Any ideas what you'll do?'

'No. Well, maybe. There is something, only...' May's voice trailed off.

Curious, Jess looked at her. May's face was bright red, and she looked as unsure and uncertain as she had when she had been new to the WAAF. 'Spit it out, May. Whatever it is can't be that bad.' A funny thought struck her. 'Let me guess, doing the village panto gave you a taste for acting, and now you want to be the British Katharine Hepburn?'

'Don't be silly.'

'Then what is this mysterious dream job? No, wait – you want to be a Tiller girl. You've got the legs for it.'

'Idiot.' May grabbed a clump of grass and flung it at Jess. Most of it landed in Jess's hair while some slid down her neck.

Jess squealed as she felt a tickling sensation creep towards her shoulder blades. 'You beast! I think there's a spider down my back.'

After much giggling on Evie and May's part and squirming on Jess's, she managed to rescue a tiny money spider before it could crawl beneath the back of her swim-suit. She blew it off her hand. 'Don't think you can distract us from your future plans, May. Own up. You owe me.'

'Promise you won't laugh.' After Evie and Jess assured her they wouldn't, May took a deep breath. 'Well, doing the panto didn't give me a taste for acting, but there was something else.' May turned her flaming face to the ground. She addressed her next words to an ant that had climbed to the tip of a blade of grass. 'I really enjoyed the writing. I've been writing stories ever since.'

'But that's wonderful. Why haven't you ever shown us?'

'Oh, they were really bad at first. I used to get so frustrated that I could never make the words match the images in my head. I'm getting better, though, and recently I've wondered if I would be able to sell stories to magazines.'

'You'll never know until you try,' Evie said. 'May, that's marvellous. I'd love to read something of yours whenever you feel ready to show someone else.'

'Me too,' Jess said. 'I know they'll be brilliant. All the best bits of the panto were the ones you wrote. You've got real talent.'

When May turned her face to look at her friends, Jess could see a suspicion of tears in her eyes. 'You really think so?'

'Course we do. We know you're a star, even if you doubt it.'

'I thought you would all laugh at me.'

'Now why on earth would we do that? I've read your stuff, remember. I know you're good.' Then Jess paused. 'Wait. So all those nights you would sit up in bed, writing away, you weren't writing to Peter but writing stories?'

'Yes. Well, I was writing to Peter too.'

'So that's me sorted out being a maths scholar, and May as an internationally renowned author.' Evie broke off and ducked when May threw another handful of grass in her direction. 'Sorry, May. I should have said you were going to be an internationally renowned *award-winning* author. Come on, Jess. You must have some thought for what you want to do after the war. I thought you loved acting.' Evie had been brushing grass from her legs; now she paused and frowned at Jess.

'I do. I've been out of it for five years, though.' That was a long time in show business. 'I'd find it difficult to get work now.'

May spoke up. 'You were brilliant as Cinderella.' She was referring to the pantomime Jess had organised during their first Christmas in the WAAF. 'They'd be mad not to give you work.'

'You're a pal, May.' Jess flashed her a smile. 'I might give it a go. I'll have to think about it.'

'There's still plenty of time to decide,' Evie said. 'I hate to break it to you both, but the war's not over yet, and who knows how long it will last?' She pulled her shirt from the bundle of clothes beside her, and her watch tumbled onto the grass. When she picked it up she gave a gasp. 'Oh my goodness. We need to get a move on if we're going to get any sleep before dinner.'

As they dressed and then made the return walk through the fields, Jess couldn't shake off the unsettled feeling brought on by their talk of life after the war. Evie and May seemed to have everything mapped out: the WAAF until the end of the war followed by marriage and work they loved. Although she was happy for them, she wished she had some idea what the future held for her.

When the girls arrived back at Bentley Manor it was to find the anteroom abuzz with news that quite threw Evie's bombshell out of Jess's head.

Gracie Metcalfe, one of the other filterers, dashed up, collaring the three friends before they'd had a chance to put away their gear. 'Have you heard?' The young woman's voice, so controlled in the Filter Room, quavered with excitement. 'There's a film crew coming to Bentley Priory. They're filming a morale-boosting drama about the RAF, and they want to shoot some scenes showing real WAAFs at work.'

'You're kidding.' Jess gripped Gracie's arm. 'Which WAAFs?' Gracie bounced on the spot, looking more like an exuberant schoolgirl than an officer. 'That's the best bit. Wait till you hear. They've managed to get a cameraman who's gone through the whole rigmarole of signing the Official Secrets Act, and he's going to shoot some footage in the Filter Room. And guess who's on watch when they're filming?'

Jess froze, not daring to hope. 'Not—?'

Gracie was already nodding, her eyes huge. 'A Watch!'

Jess whooped and performed an impromptu jig with Gracie in front of the fireplace.

'I don't believe it,' she said, when they stopped for breath. 'After all that time I tried and failed to break into films, I'm going to be on one now I'm in the WAAF.'

'We'll only be in the background,' Gracie warned. 'They're filming the scenes with the actors in the grounds and we won't be involved with those.'

'I don't care. I can tell my Auntie Vera I made it into a movie at last.'

'Do we have to be in it?' This from May. 'I don't want to be in a film. It was bad enough doing a village pantomime.'

'Are you kidding? With your looks, they'll be wanting you in every shot.' May's confidence had improved considerably over the years, but she still found it difficult to accept that people turned to take a second look when she entered a room not because they found her height amusing but because her looks had a beauty and elegance reminiscent of a young Katharine Hepburn.

Gracie wasn't finished. 'Anyway, I haven't got to the good part yet.'

'There's more? What?' Jess found it hard to believe anything could be more exciting.

'Wait until you hear which actor is playing the lead role.'

'Who?'

'Leonard Steele.'

A wave of dizziness struck, forcing Jess to clutch the back of an armchair. Thankfully May's reaction distracted Gracie from Jess's shock. 'Leonard Steele? He's gorgeous. I loved him in *Hearts of the Highlands*. What do you think, Jess? What's your favourite Leonard Steele film?'

May had given her time to recover her composure, and now she was able to speak without her voice betraying her shock. 'I liked him in *The Hellfire Murders* best.' She beamed at Gracie. 'Such exciting news. Anyway, I must wash off this pond weed before dinner.'

Smiling so broadly her face ached, she fled from the anteroom, her mind in a whirl. Whatever happened, she must take great care not to run into Leonard Steele.

Chapter Six

Jess's fears subsided when she returned to duty with the rest of A Watch at midnight. There was no way Leonard Steele – or Leo, as she had always known him – would be in the Filter Room at midnight. Even when someone came to film the WAAFs at work, she doubted Leo would be there. Jess couldn't imagine permission being given for anything other than one cameraman in the Filter Room, and even then, he wouldn't be allowed to record anything he heard. She expected his scenes would be recorded in the grounds of Bentley Priory, so as long as she kept her wits about her, she should be able to avoid him.

There was a thousand-bomber raid that night, and Jess was grateful for something to keep her busy. The earlier watch had already tracked the bombers as they left their bases along the east coast and now they were on the alert for their return. It was always a tense time, counting back the bombers and praying that none had been lost. They also had to keep an eye on stragglers in case they were in difficulty. Knowing that it had been Milan in one of the ditched aircraft she had been tracking made her all the more aware of the importance of their job. Jess knew there were girls on duty that night who had sweethearts and husbands in bomber crews and they would be painfully aware that their loved ones were probably out there.

It was an exhausting night. Apart from a brief break she was allowed at 0300 hours, when she went to the canteen on the third floor at Hill House for a restorative cup of tea, she was needed on duty to filter the tracks.

When they were finally relieved the next morning, Jess emerged into the sunlight and walked through the gardens, her feet dragging with exhaustion. She didn't know how she was going to manage to stay awake through the day, but she knew from experience that she would find it impossible to sleep through the night unless she managed to hold out.

'Coming to the mess for breakfast?' May caught her up, yawning. Evie was not far behind. 'We thought we'd go to the Spring Ponds for a dip later.'

Jess flopped onto a bench and stretched out her stiff arms. 'I'll catch you up,' she said. 'I'll sit here for a bit and let the sun warm my neck. I ache all over.' It was an occupational hazard of spending a long watch leaning over the table at awkward angles.

She watched May and Evie stroll through the grounds then she shifted so the sun was on her back. Closing her eyes, she rotated her shoulders and tilted her head from side to side to ease the muscles.

'Well, well, well. Jess Halloway, as I live and breathe. Looking more delectable than ever in uniform.'

She would recognise that cultured accent anywhere. It had set women swooning from London to Los Angeles and from Aberdeen to Adelaide. The dread that had eased during the long hours of the night watch now returned with a sickening lurch. She opened her eyes and gazed up at the young man towering over her. An impossibly handsome man with thick, wavy brown hair, a pencil moustache and soulful brown eyes. Looks that had earned him the title of the next Errol Flynn. As a naive seventeen-year-old she hadn't stood a chance. It was six years since Jess had last seen him; age had, if anything, improved his looks. As did the RAF uniform with the band on the sleeve proclaiming him to hold the rank of Flying Officer. No wings, though, so Milan beat him there.

She rose, ignoring her aching muscles and exhaustion. *Shoulders back, chin up and sparkle.* 'Leo,' she said. 'How nice to see you again.' She fixed a smile on her face, praying it hid her dread. Whatever happened, Leo must never discover he was the father of her child.

'When did we last see each other?' Leo ran a finger along the line of his moustache. 'I suppose it must have been at the end of *All Manor of Murder*.' He named the play that should have been Jess's big break.

She gave Leo her brightest smile. If he was going to ignore the fact that she had run away without even saying goodbye, she wasn't going to remind him. 'About then, I suppose,' she said, as though it wasn't a date that loomed large in her memory, forever to be associated with her failure and shame. It had broken her heart to run away from her first love. The only thing that had strengthened her resolve was the certainty that it was the right thing to do. While she had been naive, she hadn't been so naive as to imagine he was in love with her, and she couldn't take the chance of telling him now about Hannah in case he tried to take her away from Vera and Jack.

She made a gesture that took in his uniform. 'I didn't know you'd joined the RAF.'

'Thought I'd better sign up and do my bit, you know. Joined the RAF Film Production Unit.' This was a unit attached to the RAF that produced propaganda films. 'When the film studio contacted the RAF for permission to set some of the scenes here, they insisted the studio recruit actors and crew who were serving members, so here I am.'

'Here you are,' Jess echoed, fighting to keep the bitterness from her voice. 'Well, it was lovely to meet you again but I have duties to attend to.'

'Of course. I'm surprised to see you in the WAAF. I'd have thought you would join ENSA.'

She had considered the Entertainments National Service Association, of course, but at the time the entertainment business had held too many painful associations. 'I wanted to try something different.'

'What – operating a filing cabinet?'

'As it happens, I—' Jess bit off the words, remembering her signature on the Official Secrets Act just in time. 'Well, my work may be clerical, but it has to be done.'

'Of course. Then I won't keep you, but it would be good to catch up. Over dinner tonight?'

'I'm busy. Got a date.'

'You can't break it for the sake of an old friend?'

The only way she could get through this was by channelling righteous indignation. 'I'm not breaking a date with a pilot who risks his life daily and whose time isn't his own.'

Leo flinched and Jess could have kicked herself. He had clearly inferred that she thought less of him for taking a non-combatant role, and she hadn't meant that at all.

She rose. Somehow she couldn't summon the cheery, flirty Jess who usually saw her through awkward encounters; it seemed best to end the meeting before she said anything else he might take as an insult. 'Well, I must dash before I miss breakfast. Lovely to see you again.'

She walked away on trembling legs without waiting for his reply.

Why did he have to turn up when she was exhausted and unprepared? If only she had gone with Evie and May, she would have missed him, had time to work out how to act when their paths crossed.

A group of chattering aircraftwomen approached, slowing when they drew level and saluted her. Jess returned the salute, praying she had composed her features enough not to reveal the jumble of emotions and memories assailing her. Uppermost was her sense of shame and failure as she had slammed the door on the train that was to take her away from London and her life in the theatre. When the carriage door had crashed closed with brutal finality, she had finally given way to the tears she had held back during the painful weeks when she had tried to deny what the changes in her body were telling her.

What would her life be like had she not given in to Leo and fallen pregnant? Would she now be a famous actress? Of course, such thoughts led to more guilt and shame, because she loved Hannah and couldn't imagine life without her in it.

Anyway, she was now doing valued work that saved lives. Work that had led her to the best friends she had ever had. She wouldn't have missed it for the world.

Nevertheless, Leo's appearance brought back other memories: the smell of greasepaint; the flutter in the pit of her stomach as she waited in the wings for her cue; bowing to an applauding audience, knowing she had helped transport them far away from the worries of their daily lives for an hour or two. She had turned her back on all that when she had left London to have Hannah in secret. While she knew she had made the right decision, she couldn't help a tinge of regret over all she had lost. On impulse, she crossed the road and walked up Little Common, still too heartsore to face her friends. Usually she loved to look at the cottages lining the lane when she walked this way, enjoying the feel of being out in the countryside instead of a London suburb. However, this time her head was too full to pay much attention to her surroundings.

She shouldn't have insulted Leo. Although he might not be a high-ranking officer, he would have influence. He could make trouble for her. What should she do? Go back and apologise? Or was there a danger she might mention Hannah?

Only when she reached the first pool did her thoughts begin to calm. She strolled around the bank, letting the gentle sigh of the trees ease her mind. There was something about the tranquillity of this place that never failed to work its magic on her. Finally she sat on the bank and gazed across the water, admiring the reflection of the dark green leaves against the clear blue sky.

No good could come of seeking out Leo now, she realised. She was too tired. Tired and somewhat emotional after a long watch where thirty bombers had failed to return. That was thirty bomber crews who were now either prisoners or dead. If she sought out Leo now, she would be unable to hold her emotion in check, and who knew what she might blurt out? She couldn't risk him finding out about Hannah; there was no predicting how he would react to finding out he had a daughter.

No. She would, no doubt, run into him again now he was filming here. When she did, she would apologise for her hasty words and be civil to him. Do nothing to arouse his suspicion. After all, he couldn't have seriously wanted a date with her. Important men like Leonard Steele didn't waste time pursuing women who had run away from them years before. He would be gone soon enough, and she could try to forget her failure and shame.

–

Her meeting with Leo clouded what would otherwise have been a perfect day. Her stomach had been in knots, meaning she had been unable to force down much breakfast. However, the walk with Evie and May to the Spring Ponds in the late summer sunshine had gone a long way to ease her fears. As they lay on the banks after a swim, letting the sunshine and the sighing of the leaves soothe away the stresses of the night, Jess ran over the meeting in her mind for what must have been the thousandth time.

'Is everything all right, Jess?' Evie was propped on one elbow, eyeing her with concern.

'I'm right as rain. Why?'

'You look a little jumpy.'

Too right she was jumpy. Evie would be jumpy too if she worried that a former lover might suddenly stroll out from behind a tree and, with a few well-chosen words, turn her life upside down. While part of her wondered if she was doing Evie an injustice – if she would understand and be forgiving of the mistakes Jess had made in the past – she simply couldn't risk it. Evie and May were the best friends she had ever had and she didn't want to lose them. Evie came from a respectable family. Jess knew she would be shocked to learn Jess had had a child out of wedlock. Of course, May must have seen the seamier side of life, growing up with a father who had involvement with criminal gangs in Birmingham. Yet Jess didn't want to put her in a position where she shared a close secret with one of her friends and not with the other.

She opened her mouth to make some excuse or other about finding it hard to unwind after a fraught watch. Before she could say anything, May spoke up. 'I think Jess is just eager to get to her date with Milan this afternoon.'

Jess seized on this excuse. 'Hardly a date. Milan asked if I'd like to take a walk with him this afternoon and I said yes.' If she made a show of being put out by being teased about Milan, she knew her friends would try and make her talk about Milan. She'd far rather talk about him than confess what had upset her that morning.

Evie took the bait. She gave a dramatic sigh and said, 'How romantic. Just you and Milan walking hand in hand through the fields. No. Doesn't sound like a date at all.'

'In my view,' Jess said, 'it's not a proper date unless it involves dinner and dancing.'

'If you take that definition, I've hardly had any dates with Alex,' Evie said.

'Nor me,' May added.

Jess snorted. 'I should hope not. Peter would have something to say if he discovered you'd been going out with Alex.'

And so the morning passed in teasing and laughter.

Chapter Seven

Despite Jess having firmly stuck to her opinion that a walk couldn't constitute a date, she had to admit to a thrill of anticipation as she brushed her hair and fixed her makeup after lunch. When she arrived at the agreed meeting spot at the corner of Warren Lane, Milan was already there, attracting appreciative looks from a couple of WAAFs she knew from the Filter Room. They saluted him, and Jess could have sworn she saw one of the airwomen wink at him. Jess didn't waste any time in marching up to Milan, forcing the giggling girls to salute, and linking arms with him.

'I'm not late, am I?' she asked. The WAAFs cast her envious glances then drifted away.

'I was early.' As ever, his soft accent made her pulse quicken. And that was before he treated her to a crooked smile that sent a thrill from the nape of her neck to the tips of her toes. 'I wanted the pleasure of watching you walk.'

It was a good thing she was already holding his arm or her knees might have given way. She couldn't even think of a snappy riposte, which was unheard of for her. 'I bet you say that to all the girls.' It was such a corny line it made her cringe.

'No. Just you.'

It took a moment for Jess to recover from the impact of the words spoken in a matter-of-fact tone. 'Then you're lucky you've got me all to yourself today.' She gave his arm a tug to pull him towards the footpath. 'Shall we go?'

Milan didn't budge. 'One moment. In Czechoslovakia it is the custom to kiss when we meet.'

'I've never known you be a stickler for custom.'

'Perhaps that is where I go wrong.'

She shrugged, trying not to appear too keen. 'Far be it for me to go against tradition.' It occurred to her that she should assure him he had never done anything wrong. However, before she could insist that the fault had all been on her side, he stooped and kissed her on both cheeks. For a brief moment her senses swam at the soft brush of his lips against her skin and the faint scent of lemon soap and tobacco. Then he stepped back, looking smug, and held out his arm. '*Now* we go.'

Jess, two burning spots on her cheeks where his mouth had touched her, tucked her arm back through his. 'There's a custom I could get used to,' she said, when she could speak. Ridiculous how a simple kiss on the cheek should scatter her wits to the four winds. She really needed to get a grip.

They struck out across one of the many paths that criss-crossed the common. Soon they were out of earshot of the noise of Stanmore, and the only sounds were the breeze stirring the leaves and the twitter of birdsong. The path they had selected was lined with trees and brambles, and it felt as though they were walking right out in the country instead of an area of London. It was so reminiscent of the walks they had used to take at Amberton, Jess half expected to hear the throaty roar of Hurricanes flying overhead. She said as much to Milan, and soon they were chatting easily about the friends they had both known. The years fell away, and Jess moved closer, walking pressed against his side as she had always done at Amberton.

'Here's another custom I used to enjoy.' Milan pulled them to a halt beside a tangle of blackberry bushes. The brambles were heavy with the shiny dark purple berries. Milan picked a few and offered them to Jess. She tasted one gingerly, expecting it to be tart, but it burst on her tongue in an explosion of sweetness.

'This reminds me of blackberry picking with my Auntie Vera,' she said, picking more berries until her fingers were stained purple with the juice.

Milan's brow furrowed. 'I remind you of your Auntie Vera? That is not a good thing to hear on a date.'

Jess gave him a little shove. 'Go on. You're just fishing for compliments.' She reached for a cluster of blackberries that hung on a branch just out of reach. 'Anyway, it's no bad thing to remind me of Auntie Vera. She's the strongest person I know. The kindest, too, but she'd face down a herd of stampeding buffalo if they threatened someone she loved.'

'Ah, a lioness. She sounds like my sister.' Milan leaned past Jess to grasp the bramble she was trying to reach. He pulled it closer to Jess so she could pick the berries, steadying himself with an arm around her shoulders. Jess felt an overpowering wave of longing, making her quite light-headed. She had to force herself to pick the black-berries instead of lean back and breathe in his warm citrusy scent. She loved the sensation of being enfolded in his arms. A bramble thicket on Stanmore Common was a far cry from the Midsummer dance at Amberton, but she could almost hear the band playing, feel his strong arms around her as he guided her around the dance floor.

Then all the reasons why she had broken off their relationship punched her in the gut. Nothing had changed. She would never not be Hannah's mother. She would never be able to undo the mistakes she had made. She was damaged goods. That was what she had always heard people muttering darkly about women in the same situation as her. No man would want to be with her when they learnt the truth, yet if she stayed with Milan she would have to confess.

'Tell me about your sister. What is her name?' she asked, moving aside so he would have to release the bramble and remove the arm he'd slung around her shoulders. She missed the warmth of his body the moment they moved apart.

'She is called Eliška.'

'Elishka,' Jess repeated, trying out the unfamiliar sounds almost absently while her thoughts were occupied trying to work out why it seemed so wrong to conceal her past from Milan. 'What a lovely name. Is she older or younger than you?'

'Older. By half an hour.'

It took Jess a moment to work it out. 'Oh, you're twins.' She tried and failed to imagine a woman with Milan's features. 'I've heard twins can sense things from each other, even when they are far apart. Does that happen with you?'

'No. I wish it did. Then I would know if she was well.'

Jess wished she hadn't asked. It had been natural curiosity but she'd completely forgotten what Milan had told her the other day about not knowing if his sister and nephew were still alive. 'I'm sorry,' she said, putting a hand on his arm. 'It must be awful not knowing. I can't imagine how that feels.'

Milan gave a smile that looked forced. 'They say the Allies are heading for Berlin, that the Germans cannot hold out for much longer. Soon I will be able to go back and find them.'

It seemed as though everyone was thinking about what they would do after the war. 'You will definitely return to Czechoslovakia after the war, then?'

'I must find Eliška and Franta, my nephew. I could not live with myself not knowing. But—' He gave her an odd look and hesitated as though considering whether to say something else. Then he gave a dismissive wave. 'Who knows what will happen next.'

'I hope they are all right.' Jess shivered. Reports were already filtering through from the liberated areas of France, about what life had been like under the Nazis. Czechoslovakia had been occupied for longer than France and who knew how long it would be before it was freed? She remembered hearing about the horrific reprisals carried out upon the Czechs after the assassination of Reinhard Heydrich. She had been out of touch with Milan and his compatriots by then but she had been haunted by how it must have felt for them to learn of the mass killings. She tried to imagine her reaction if everyone in Poplar had been massacred and found it impossible to envisage.

Not long after they decided that they had eaten their fill of blackberries and should leave some to the blackbird that had perched on a nearby spray, eyeing them with sideways jerks of the head.

'I must leave soon,' Milan said with a glance at his watch. Jess nodded and they walked back along the path while Milan told her more about his life in Prague and his dreams of finishing his studies. 'Although whether they will want me back when I have not picked up a violin in over five years, I do not know,' he finished.

'The same with me and acting,' Jess said. 'It's going to be strange returning to civilian life.' They were at the entrance to Stanmore Underground station by this time, where they were to part ways. However, Jess didn't release Milan's arm, reluctant to say goodbye.

'You know,' she said, when Milan made no attempt to move either, 'It's a British custom to kiss when we say goodbye.'

'Then we must,' Milan said, the corners of his eyes crinkling. 'It would be bad luck to break tradition.' He moved closer, placing his hands on her shoulders. 'Although I wish we did not have to say goodbye just yet.' His voice was pitched low and sent shivers down her spine.

She raised herself on tiptoe to meet him halfway. For one heart-pounding moment she thought he was going to kiss her on the lips. Then a group of young women dashed out of the station, jostling Jess and Milan as they ran past.

The moment spoiled, Jess kissed Milan on the cheek. 'Well, goodbye,' she said.

She made to turn away, but Milan gripped her hand. 'We will do this again? Today has been like… *oáza*. Oasis,' he corrected.

'I'd like that.'

The smile he gave her in reply kindled a glow that continued to warm her even after she had watched him disappear into the station.

Her head full of the date – it had definitely been a date even if it didn't meet her usual definition – she didn't want to return straight away to the mess. There was still plenty of time before dinner, and she didn't want to face Evie and May's questions until she'd worked some things out in her mind.

She wanted to see him again. Of that she was sure. She couldn't think of any date she'd enjoyed as much as her walk with Milan. She had been wined and dined by officers from all the various postings where she had worked since leaving Amberton; some of the officers had gone to great lengths to impress, finding restaurants that still managed to produce a varied menu despite rationing, even presenting her with luxury gifts such as nylons and scented soaps that were so hard to find these days. Even so, none of those dates could match today. A warm glow enveloped her as she relived every second of the walk.

She wandered, aimlessly at first, past shops and houses. Then it occurred to her that she could buy gifts for Auntie Vera and Hannah. She could never do enough to show her gratitude to Vera for being there when Jess had gone to her aunt in a distraught state when she had realised she was pregnant. Vera had arranged everything, and after discussion with her husband they had agreed to take Hannah as their own much-longed-for child. It had involved an elaborate deception, with Jess being sent away to a rented house in Suffolk before she started to show, and Vera announcing her pregnancy before joining Jess in Suffolk 'for the sake of her health'. Whether any of their neighbours had guessed the truth, Jess didn't know, but no one had said anything in her hearing.

Hannah had been born in January 1939. Giving her to Vera had been heartbreaking but Jess had known it was for the best. She had tried to pick up more acting jobs once she was fully recovered, but her heart hadn't been in it. When war had broken out, after much discussion with Vera, they had decided the best thing for her was to join the forces. Not a day had gone by since then that she didn't miss Hannah, but she knew it was best for everyone if she got her life in order. It was a comfort to know that Hannah couldn't hope for a better mother than Vera.

She found some pretty hair ribbons and a book of fairy tales for Hannah. It was while she was gazing into the window of Stoneleigh and Swift Antiques, wondering if Vera would like a pretty bone china teacup and saucer, painted with pink rosebuds, that she saw it. Propped on the back shelf, half hidden behind a mahogany lap desk, was a violin in its own case. At once she thought of Milan and his lost violin.

She couldn't really explain it to herself but stepping out with Milan was more like spending time with a friend – it wasn't all about being given gifts and the glamour of being seen on the arm of a handsome pilot. Somehow with Milan she wanted him to be happy. If he had his heart set on being a concert violinist, she wanted to help him achieve his dream.

There was no price visible, though. That couldn't be a good sign. She pushed open the door, the shrill jangle of the bell making her jump. A middle-aged woman wearing a floral dress and cerise cardigan walked through the door at the rear of the shop. 'Can I help you?' she asked.

'Yes, please. I'd like to see the rosebud teacup and saucer that's in the window, thank you.'

The assistant got the cup and saucer down for Jess to inspect. One of the rosebuds on the saucer was a little scratched, which was probably why the price was so affordable. Jess, certain Vera would like it, said she would take it. The woman went behind the counter and pulled out sheets of newspaper to wrap the cup and saucer in. Jess summoned her courage and said, 'I couldn't help noticing the violin in the window.'

The woman's expression changed. It became more guarded, somehow, and tension seemed to clench the corner of her mouth.

Jess hesitated but she had already started so she might as well get to the point. 'Is it for sale? There was no price ticket.'

The woman looked her up and down. 'Who do you want it for – you?' Her voice had lost its former polite, friendly tone. It sounded harsh, a little strained, as though she struggled to hold back some powerful emotion.

'It's not for me. It's for a friend,' Jess replied. She would have elaborated, but the woman put her hand to her mouth, which had begun to quiver.

'I'm sorry. I didn't mean to upset you. I don't even know why I'm asking. I doubt I'd be able to afford it.'

The woman shook her head then flapped her hand across her mouth which was tightly shut. It was clear she was close to tears.

'Oh dear.' Jess peered past the poor woman to the back room to see if there was anyone she could call on for help, but it appeared the shop assistant was alone. There was, however, a little electric stove and a kettle. Jess made up her mind. She joined the woman behind the counter, took her arm and led her to a chair. 'I'm so sorry I upset you,' she repeated. 'The least I can do is make you a cup of tea.'

The woman was incapable of saying anything, but she nodded her head, so Jess slipped into the back room. The kettle was already full; Jess put it on the stove and rummaged through the items on a crammed shelf above the stove to find a cup, tea and sugar. A little jug of milk stood in a bowl of water to keep it cool.

When the kettle gave a shrill, steady whistle, Jess spooned tea into a chipped china teapot and poured on the boiling water. She glanced into the main shop to ask the woman how she liked her tea only to see her hunched over, face in her hands and shoulders shaking. Deciding to give the woman time to regain her composure, Jess allowed the tea to brew good and strong before pouring out a cup and adding milk. She picked up the sugar basin then hesitated a moment, unwilling to waste such a scarce commodity. Then she decided if anyone needed a good dose of sugar right now it was this poor woman, so she added a heaped spoonful to the cup and stirred.

The woman was dabbing her reddened eyes with a damp handkerchief when Jess returned to the main room. Jess noticed a gold band on her ring finger. 'Here you go, Mrs...'

'Swift,' the woman supplied, 'but call me Kathleen. It seems silly to stick to formalities when you've seen me in such a state.'

'I'm Jess. Drink this. A good cup of strong tea can't solve all your problems but it will make you feel a bit better.'

'I don't know what you must think of me,' Kathleen said, sipping the tea. Jess was pleased to see some colour had returned to her pale cheeks. 'I do hope I'm not delaying you. You work up at Bentley Priory?' She made a gesture that took in Jess's cap and uniform.

'Oh, don't worry about that,' Jess replied. 'I do work there, but I don't have to be back on duty until tomorrow morning.'

'Well, you're very kind giving up your free time to look after me. You must be so busy. My husband is in the RAF, you see. He joined up as a mechanic at the start of the war and is full of praise at how the WAAFs can do all the work the men do, and better very often.'

Jess grinned. 'It took some of the men a while to work that out. I'm glad we've got your husband on side.'

There was a pause while Kathleen sipped her tea, then she said in a low voice, 'Is it true that Leonard Steele is making a film at Bentley Priory?'

Jess considered her answer but, after all, it wasn't part of her work so there was no reason she couldn't speak of it. 'It is. I saw him this morning.'

Kathleen clapped a hand to her mouth. 'Oh my goodness. What was he like? I think I would have fainted if I'd seen him.'

There was no point in destroying her illusions. 'He was lovely. So charming and friendly.'

'I've seen all his films. My husband took me to see *Hearts of the Highlands* when he was last home on leave.' Then her face crumpled. 'That was when he told me I should sell our Danny's violin.'

Jess patted her shoulder awkwardly, sure she knew what was coming.

'He was our boy.' Kathleen pulled her hanky out from her sleeve and wiped her eyes again. 'He was studying music but when the war started, he joined the RAF just like his father. He was a good mechanic. He could have been one of the ground crew, but he had his heart set on flying. He was so happy when he earned his wings and was made pilot of a bomber crew.'

Jess's stomach lurched. She knew only too well how dangerous the life of a bomber pilot was.

'He was shot down over the sea two years ago,' Kathleen said. 'His crew were rescued. Not him. He drowned before they could get to him.'

'I'm so sorry,' Jess said. She had been working as a Filter Plotter then. She wondered if she had plotted Danny Swift's bomber. There had been so many lost over the years.

Kathleen pulled herself upright and squared her shoulders. 'I mustn't live in the past, though. Keeping his things won't bring him back. That's what my husband told me.'

'But if you're not ready…'

Kathleen shook her head. 'No. I am. I'd only just put the violin in the window, you see. I thought if I didn't put a price on it, people would only ask about it if they really wanted it. I do so want it to go to someone who would treat it well, you know.' She drained her teacup and set it aside. 'So tell me about this friend of yours.'

And, much to her surprise, Jess found herself telling Kathleen all about Milan. 'And so when I saw your son's violin in the window, I thought of Milan straight away,' she concluded. 'The war has taken so much from him, I don't want him to lose his music as well.'

'And it shan't,' Kathleen said. Her lost expression was gone, replaced by a look of determination. 'I think it was a sign, you coming to ask about Danny's violin the day I put it in the window. I've lost my son but I do at least have a home. I would like your young man to have Danny's violin.'

'Oh, that's very kind but—' Jess hesitated. She had only wanted to enquire after the price. In all probability, it would be beyond her means. She shifted from foot to foot, unsure how to phrase it.

Kathleen, however, seemed to have read her mind. 'Now don't you worry about the price. I don't want any money. It makes me happy to know it's going to someone who loves music and will cherish it as much as my boy did. I couldn't ask for better than that.'

Now it was Jess's turn to blink away tears. 'Oh, Mrs Swift, I couldn't.'

'I told you to call me Kathleen. And you most certainly can. If your young man ends up delighting audiences with his music then in a way, Danny can live on through it.' Jess opened her mouth to protest; Kathleen cut her off. 'I won't take no for an answer.'

'That's—' Jess cleared her throat to ease the sudden tightness 'I don't know how to thank you. Are you sure there's nothing I can give you in return?'

'Nothing. Well—' a faint blush tinged Kathleen's cheeks. 'I don't suppose… No. Forget it.'

'Tell me. You've been so kind. If there's anything I can do in return I'd love to help.'

'You couldn't get Leonard Steele's autograph for me, could you?'

It took all of Jess's acting experience to keep her smile from fading. 'I'll make sure of it,' she promised, 'even if I have to camp outside his dressing room.'

Jess left Stoneleigh and Swift with a newspaper-wrapped cup and saucer in one hand and swinging the violin case in the other. While she couldn't wait to see Milan's expression when she presented it to him, she dreaded approaching Leo for the autograph. Leonard Steele wasn't a man to give something away for nothing.

Chapter Eight

Jess's promise to Kathleen weighed heavily on her mind the next morning as they crossed the extensive grounds of Hill House on their way to the Filter Room. Her feet dragged. The last thing she wanted to do was speak to Leo again.

'Careful, Jess,' Evie said. 'I nearly walked into you. Whatever is the matter with you this morning?'

'It's obvious,' May said, strolling up beside them. 'Her head's full of Milan and how he's going to thank her for the violin.'

If only she had the luxury of daydreaming about Milan. It had been impossible to hide the violin from Evie and May when she had arrived back at the mess the previous afternoon, so she'd been forced to tell them the whole tale. Both of her friends had been convinced getting Milan the violin was a huge romantic gesture instead of, as Jess tried to convince them, a complete accident. Still, while they were fixated on her relationship with Milan, perhaps it would distract them from questioning her too thoroughly about Leo when she was forced to reveal she knew him.

Evie and May were still teasing her when they entered the Filter Room. Jess, as was her habit, glanced at the sector clock the moment she took her position. This helped her make sense quickly of the order of the various tracks on the table. As she glanced up, something looked out of place on the balcony, making her look twice. A cameraman in RAF uniform was setting up a film camera on its tripod. A uniformed woman was handling a powerful lamp, shining it where the cameraman indicated. She didn't know how the film makers had persuaded the top brass to let them film in the Filter Room, but judging from the expressions on the faces of the Controller and Filter Officer, they weren't happy at having their domain taken over. Jess automatically put her hand to her head to check her hair was in place. She was glad she had taken extra care with her hair and makeup that morning. Despite her various worries, she couldn't deny the excitement prickling her spine at the prospect of being involved, in however small a way, in a film that would soon hit the cinemas. While she might have been forced to leave behind the world of acting, she had never forgotten its allure and the way the most mundane of actions made the pulse quicken when they were part of a play or film. As she examined the table, she was painfully aware of the camera and found she had the same heightened sense of awareness of her posture, actions and expression that she always felt when she was acting.

The Controller addressed A Watch as they took their places. 'You will notice we have visitors today. Rest assured they have signed the Official Secrets Act and won't be recording sound. As I'm sure you've heard, NMG Films are making a picture about the Battle of Britain and have been given special permission to film scenes with real men and women of the RAF and WAAF in the background. All we ask is that you do your jobs as normal and don't look at the camera.'

Once Jess had relieved her counterpart from C Watch, there was little time for self-consciousness. Several 'Divers' were reported in short order, and she was fully occupied in tracking them and ensuring accurate information reached the gunners at the coast. As ever, she felt a spike of fear when flying bombs appeared on the track and could never rest easy until word came back they had been destroyed. Although London was huge, she was always conscious of a dread that this one, if it got past the defences on the coast, would hit the house in Poplar where Vera and Hannah were.

During a lull in the action in the early afternoon, she was relieved for a short break. Having been too worked up to manage much breakfast, she was now aware of a gnawing ache in her stomach. If she was quick, she would have time for a bite to eat at the canteen. Pulling on her cap, she hurried across the gardens to Hill House and climbed the stairs to the third floor.

Getting food from this canteen was something of a gamble. Last week she had been offered marmite and cabbage sandwiches. Today, when she sat at an empty table with a plate of sandwiches and a cup of tea, she gingerly prised apart the curling bread on her plate to see what delights awaited her. It looked like spam and onion. With a mental shrug, she took a bite. It should keep Leo at arm's length if she saw him this afternoon.

As if summoned by her thoughts, the man himself appeared at the entrance of the canteen. He paused for a moment, perfectly framed in the doorway, and a ripple of whispers worked its way through the canteen as WAAFs nudged neighbours, and heads turned to regard the handsome star.

Leo's gaze fell on Jess. He strode through the room, pausing to smile and wink at the giggling WAAFs as he passed, but never allowing himself to be diverted from his goal. Jess put her sandwich down, praying her lipstick hadn't smudged. The next moment she was hating herself for having that thought. She wasn't interested in Leo any more, so why worry about her appearance?

'Well, well, well,' Leo said, pulling out a chair opposite Jess and sitting down. 'Two days in a row. One could almost believe we were fated to be together.'

Once again, Jess was at a loss as to why he would single her out after she had left him without a word all those years ago. She'd salved her conscience at the time by telling herself he had regarded her as no more than a pleasant diversion; now she couldn't help feeling a twinge of guilt. Had she meant more to him than she'd suspected? She bit back a retort about fate not having to work too hard to bring two people together in a canteen at lunchtime. Instead, she forced a smile and said, 'I'm glad to see you again, Leo. I wanted to apologise for yesterday. You caught me at a bad moment – I'd had a difficult night on duty.'

He gave a magnanimous wave of the hand. 'No need to apologise. I quite understand. Filing cabinet drawer got jammed?'

It took a moment for Jess to unclench the muscles in her jaw enough to answer. 'Something like that.' It was only the thought of Kathleen Swift's request that prevented her from making a sharp reply. That and the suspicion that his persistence in putting down her work might be his way of getting his own back from any hurt she had caused him. 'Anyway, I'm glad to see you today. I was hoping you would do me a favour.' She raised her voice a little. Loud enough to be heard by the WAAFs at neighbouring tables who were, not very subtly, angling their heads to overhear their conversation. 'I met a woman yesterday who had lost her son – he was a bomber pilot.

When she heard you were here, she asked if I would get your autograph for her. It would really brighten her day to know you were thinking of her.'

'Of course.' Leo pulled a dog-eared notebook from his pocket. For a moment Jess thought he would scrawl his name on a piece of the tatty paper and hand it to her. 'What's her name?' he asked, pen poised. 'I have some personalised cards back in my hotel room.' From the way he angled his body, Jess knew he was speaking more for the benefit of the onlookers than her. 'I can write her a personalised note if you would deliver it for me.'

He jotted down the name and replaced the pad and pen in his pocket with a flourish. Then he leaned across the table and lowered his voice. 'I'll give it to you over dinner tonight.'

Wonderful. A whole evening with the man whose mere presence was a constant reminder of her shameful past. Remembering Kathleen Swift's tear-streaked face, however, she could hardly refuse. She could still drive a bargain, though. 'I'll gladly have dinner with you,' she said. 'We can pop into Mrs Swift's shop on the way so you can give her your card in person.' Again, she spoke loud enough for others to hear without making it obvious.

Leo's smile didn't waver for an instant. 'I would be only too happy to meet her. It's the least I can do after her sad loss.'

—

If Leo had been less than enthusiastic about meeting Kathleen Swift, he had the good grace not to show it when they popped into Stoneleigh and Swift Antiques that evening. Kathleen was standing beside the door, her hand on the door sign, obviously about to switch it to the 'Closed' side. Her face turned the same scarlet as Jess's lipstick when she saw who was there. The sign dropped from her fingers and clattered on the floor.

'May we come in?' Jess asked. 'When Mr Steele heard of your sad loss and your kindness to me, he said he'd like to bring you his autograph in person.' She smiled sweetly at Leo, silently vowing she would make his life a misery if he acted as anything other than delighted about meeting a fan in person.

She needn't have worried. Once Kathleen had recovered enough to step away from the door and let them in, Leo stepped over the threshold, placed a hand on Kathleen's shoulder and gazed into her eyes. 'My deepest sympathies for your sad loss,' he said, his voice throbbing with concern. 'I've had the honour of working with several bomber crews, and so when Jess told me the mother of one of those gallant young men was nearby, I had to come and pay my respects.' He reached into his pocket and pulled out the card he had written out for her. It had his photograph on the front.

Kathleen took it, her eyes shining, and stammered out a few words of thanks. Jess knew that Kathleen would remember this moment for the rest of her life and would always treasure Leo's card. Kathleen had been too overcome to talk much, but Leo had done more than enough talking for the two of them, expressing his sympathy for Kathleen's loss, paying tribute to the brave bomber pilots and their crews and even, when Jess had mentioned that Kathleen's husband was in the RAF as ground crew, praising the men who kept the RAF in the skies with their hard work, calling them unsung heroes. Jess forbore to mention the hard work of the WAAFs.

Finally Leo took his leave, kissing Kathleen's hand with a gallantry Jess was sure he had borrowed from his film, *Knight of the Cross*. Jess had been about to follow him outside when Kathleen stopped her. 'I don't know how to thank you,' she said. 'When you said you might get his autograph, I never dreamed – well, this is a day that will live long in my memory.'

'It was a pleasure,' Jess replied. 'The debt is still firmly on my side after your kindness with the violin.'

'Oh, I should have asked,' Kathleen said. 'Seeing Leonard Steele at my door quite drove it from my head. How did your young man like the violin?'

Leo had been adjusting his tie by his reflection in the shop window. At mention of her young man, Jess thought he paused for a moment before resuming his task. She had considered correcting Kathleen and telling her Milan wasn't 'her' young man. However, something about Leo's reaction made her let the comment pass. 'Oh, I haven't seen him yet – he can't get another free evening until next week. I promise to bring him to see you once I've given it to him. I'm sure he'd like to meet you.'

Kathleen put her hand to her throat, clutching the golden cross pendant she wore on a chain. 'You are so good to me. That would be lovely.'

'Thank you for doing that,' Jess said to Leo after they'd left the shop and were strolling towards the centre of Stanmore. 'You were very good with her.' Indeed, she had been moved by the way he had spoken to Kathleen about the bravery and sacrifice of the bomber crews he had known. Although he was a good actor, Jess had thought his tribute had been from the heart.

'It's the least I could do,' Leo said, and offered her his arm.

Jess gave him a sideways glance as she placed her hand on his arm, feeling a twinge of disloyalty to Milan as she did so. Yet again she wondered what would have happened if she had told him she was pregnant instead of running away the moment the play they were starring in had come to the end of its run. Perhaps she had misjudged him. Maybe he would have been overjoyed.

She gave herself a mental shake. Likely story. Not three days after arriving in Suffolk, she had seen a photo of Leo in the paper. It had shown him at a theatrical gala, partnered by a well-known actress. Jess knew that tickets had been sold weeks in advance, weeks when they had been together, yet he hadn't invited her. The tears she had shed after reading the article had been the last she had shed over Leonard Steele.

Looking for an excuse to remove her hand from his arm, she pointed at the sky. 'There's a lovely sunset tonight.'

'Not as lovely as you.'

'Come off it, Leo. Don't try that line on me. I only agreed to come out with you tonight so you would give Kathleen your autograph.'

Leo clapped a hand to his chest as though he had been struck. 'Can't a fellow even compliment his date?'

'This is not a date. We go out as friends or not at all.'

'So your heart's already spoken for?'

For a horrible moment she feared Leo was about to confess he had loved her all along. When she shot him a sharp glance and saw his eyebrows raised in enquiry and no sign of disappointment, relief washed over her. 'The state of my heart is none of your business.'

'What about the young man your shop assistant mentioned? Is it *his* business?'

Jess drew breath to snap that Milan was none of Leo's business either but bit back the retort. Leo had a right to feel aggrieved about the way their relationship had ended, yet he had been surprisingly friendly. She should return the favour and not antagonise him.

She put her hand back on his arm. 'He's just a fighter pilot I got friendly with when I was stationed at Amberton. He's based at RAF Benson now.' She explained about the violin while leaving out any hint of what her feelings for Milan might be. It really was no concern of Leo's. She only belatedly noticed they had stopped outside the underground station, and Leo was fishing in his pockets for change. 'Oh, are we going into Town? I assumed we'd be eating in Stanmore.'

'Now, why would I take you out in a backwater like Stanmore when we've got the whole of London on our doorstep? When I take a beautiful woman to dinner, I do it properly.'

Jess shot him a warning glare, one eyebrow arched, and he raised his hands in mock surrender. 'I know, I know. I should have said when I take a beautiful woman to dinner *as friends*, I do it properly.'

'In that case...' Jess let him escort her into the station. Who was she to deny herself the chance of being properly wined and dined by a film star? Leo had always been fun company, and if he was able to put the past behind him then she could hardly complain. He was probably taking her out because it was good publicity for him to be seen with a WAAF officer. Well, if this was her one chance to experience the high life, Jess was going to make the most of it. There was absolutely no reason for her to feel it was disloyal to Milan.

The platform was busy with people on their way to town for the evening. Although it was a bit of a crush, Jess didn't mind. It meant Leo couldn't interrogate her about anything personal such as Milan or the reason why she had left him. As long as they avoided those subjects, she would enjoy herself.

It was certainly fun to be the centre of interest. Other people on the platform were nudging their companions, pointing to Leo. Jess caught several envious glances from the other young women. Leo took it in his stride, smiling and exchanging greetings with anyone who dared to speak to him. When they got on the train, it felt like the whole crowd tried to squeeze into the same carriage. After they had taken their seats, a blushing girl of about sixteen approached Leo. 'Are you really Leonard Steele?' she asked. When Leo nodded her face turned an even brighter scarlet. 'Please can I have your autograph?' She rummaged in her handbag as she spoke and thrust two crumpled pieces of paper at him. 'One for me and one for my friend?'

'Of course.' Leo took the paper, pulled a fountain pen from his top pocket and scrawled his name on both sheets. He handed them back to the girl, who Jess thought might explode from excitement.

'Thank you so much,' the girl said. She took a step towards her seat then hesitated and said in a breathless voice, 'You were wonderful as Captain Jack McCabe in *The Pirate's Prize.*' Then she bounded back to her friend, squealing, 'I got them, Norah!'

The girls subsided into whispers, although the furtive glances they shot towards Leo and Jess at intervals throughout the journey left Jess in no doubt as to the subject of their conversation. At one point she distinctly heard the other girl, Norah, say in a piercing whisper, 'I wonder who he's with? She's very pretty.' Jess had to admit she enjoyed the attention.

They left the train at Charing Cross, and Jess could hardly believe her luck when Leo took her to the Savoy. She clutched his arm, doing her best not to show her excitement at being led into the famous airy restaurant with its pillared walls and high ceiling. A cabaret band played on the stage, and when Leo walked in, they struck up a few bars of the theme music from his latest film. Despite there being several famous faces already present in the restaurant, a stir of interest rippled across the room as they were shown to their table. Jess could sense the eyes of all the women on her.

'They must be wondering who on earth I am,' she muttered after the waiter had handed her the menu and left them to choose. She was tickled to notice that the Savoy, just like any other restaurant these days, was forced to comply with the order from the Ministry of Food and limit its maximum charge to five shillings.

'Nonsense,' Leo said. 'The men will all be envying me for being with the best looking woman in the room.'

Considering she was one of the few women in uniform, and none of the women in civvies looked as though wartime austerity had affected their lavish wardrobes, she doubted that. Nevertheless, it was nice to be complimented.

'How long will you be filming at Bentley Priory?' she asked.

'About a month, I think. The director keeps on insisting on new story lines the more he learns about life in the RAF so he might need longer.'

More than just a few days, then. Jess didn't know whether to be apprehensive about the potential disruption to her routine, or pleased about the extra excitement and glamour.

'Talking of changes in storyline,' Leo went on, 'the director showed me the footage he filmed of the WAAFs this morning.'

'Then you'll have seen filing cabinets don't feature in my work.' She couldn't explain why, but Leo's assumption that her work was purely clerical really rankled.

Leo shrugged. 'So you put counters on a map. I stand corrected.'

'There's more to it than that.' Until now she had never regretted the secrecy surrounding the work of a WAAF whose job was designated 'clerk, special duties'. She had to forcefully remind herself of the dire consequences of being in breach of the Official Secrets Act to give her the strength to bite back the explanation of what she actually did. Maybe it was because Leo had known her when she'd been an actress, one poised on the brink of making a name for herself, but to have him think her work was mundane hurt. Or possibly it was that he made propaganda films about the RAF that showed the bravery and skill of the men while either completely ignoring the role of the WAAF, or showing the women in the background, somehow implying their work was menial. History was being written and the women's roles in it were being ignored.

'Of course there is,' Leo said. It was a good thing the waiter arrived to take their order at that point, or Leo would have been in danger of wearing the flower arrangement. 'Anyway, that's beside the point. I have news that will interest you.'

'Oh yes?' Jess decided it was pointless trying to educate Leo even if she could have told him what she did. He would never understand.

'The director picked you out of the group of girls immediately.'

'He did?' Jess leaned forward, her irritation fading. 'What did he say?'

'He was impressed. Said there was something about you the camera loved.'

When Jess had been an actress, she had dreamed of catching a director's eye and making the move from stage to screen. Though she had got a thrill from the theatre, stage actors never got the same recognition as film actors. The scene on the underground was proof of the way film actors, and the characters they played, caught the public imagination. 'It's nice to be noticed,' she said.

'Oh, he noticed you. Look, I can't promise anything, but he said something about speaking to the writers to include a WAAF in the storyline.'

'About time the WAAF got a look-in.'

'I haven't got to the good part yet.'

Suddenly Jess realised where this was leading. 'Wait. You don't mean to tell me—' She broke off as the sommelier arrived with their wine. She watched Leo's face with growing impatience as he tasted the wine and gave a nod of approval. The man then poured the wine into each of their glasses, moving with agonising slowness. Jess tapped her fingers on her knees, not daring to let herself believe her luck until Leo had spoken the words. 'Well?' she said the moment the sommelier was out of earshot.

'Nothing is definite, but the director is going to have a word with your superiors. If they agree, you'll be released from duty for a couple of weeks while we film the part.'

'Oh my goodness. You're 'avin'… *having* me on.' Jess raised her wine glass to her lips with a hand that trembled, silently berating herself for her momentary slip. Speaking in a BBC accent was almost second nature these days.

'Not a bit of it. I always said you were destined for stardom. I could never understand why you disappeared from the scene just when you were about to get your big break.'

Jess put down her drink untasted. This was the first time Leo had directly referred to the end of their relationship, and she couldn't avoid it any longer. She licked her lips, racking her brains for a suitable explanation.

Leo leaned across the table. 'Come on, Jess. We could have been London's golden couple. Why did you disappear?'

'Maybe I didn't like being in the limelight.'

Leo laughed. 'Now I know you're joking. You thrive on it.' He gestured towards the other diners. 'You can't tell me you don't love all the attention you're getting.' He held her gaze, and Jess was unable to look away. 'Come on. What's the real reason?'

She took a sip of wine to buy herself a little more time. However, she only had one clear thought: she mustn't let slip about Hannah. In the early days after Hannah had been born, Jess had wrestled with her conscience, wondering if she should inform Leo he had a daughter. However, the newspapers had regularly published photographs showing he still pursued the same wild lifestyle he had lived when she had known him, and she hadn't wanted to risk Leo taking Hannah away. While Vera and Jack didn't have much money, they showered Hannah with love, affection and stability. All things Hannah needed far more than money.

'I wanted to serve my country,' she said in the end. 'It was clear that we would soon be at war, and I wanted to do something useful.'

Leo shook his head sadly. 'A woman like you shouldn't be shut away in a back room. You owe it to the people of Britain to brighten up their lives by bringing them a little Hollywood razzle dazzle. The war has dragged on for so long. They need some sparkle in their lives.'

He regarded her over the brim of his wine glass, his eyes twinkling. 'Admit it, you've missed show-business.'

'Well... perhaps a little.' She couldn't stop her mouth from mirroring Leo's grin, though.

'Then you'll take the role?'

'I haven't been offered it yet.'

'But if you are? And I'm fairly certain you will be.'

'I'd have to see the script.' Who was she kidding? They both knew she wouldn't turn it down. Not when she had a chance to fulfil her dreams. Jess had showbiz running through her veins and she couldn't resist its pull.

Leo raised his glass in a toast. 'Here's to Jess Halloway, the newest star of the silver screen.'

There was an annoying voice in the back of her mind that wouldn't be silenced. It spoke in her voice, in the precise, clear accent she'd cultivated since joining the WAAF. Section Officer Jess Halloway reminded her not to get carried away by the glamour. She was only being offered a small speaking role in what was destined to be a morale-boosting film for the British public, not a Hollywood blockbuster. Was there another, selfish, reason why Leo was pushing her into it?

Jess Halloway the actress told Section Officer Halloway to take a running jump. She was being offered a taste of her lifelong dream, and she intended to seize it with both hands. She raised her glass in return. 'To us,' she said. 'Stars of the silver screen.'

But as she worked her way through the best of what the Savoy could offer and drank in the admiring glances sent her way, she couldn't help remembering walking on Stanmore Common with Milan, picking blackberries and laughing at their purple-stained fingers.

Chapter Nine

Jess was still bubbling over with excitement when she went on duty the next night. Her CO called her aside. 'We've had rather an unusual request concerning you,' Flight Officer Laura Morgan said. 'The director of the film unit has requested that you be released for a fortnight. They wish you to take a role in the film.'

'Yes, ma'am,' Jess said, clasping her hands so tight behind her back her fingers dug into her palms.

Morgan frowned. 'This is most irregular. If the request had been for an airwoman it would have been easier to grant. This is not the kind of work we would expect an officer to do.'

Jess's heart sank. Although she had feared the request might be denied due to her being needed in the Filter Room, she hadn't expected her officer status to cause trouble. It seemed she was continually falling foul of the expectations placed upon her as an officer. She, Evie and May had frequently giggled over their surprise when discovering a large part of their officer training had consisted of how to comport themselves in the Officers' Mess. However, she knew better than to protest. All she said was, 'I'm sorry, ma'am.'

'Nevertheless,' Morgan continued, and Jess's heart skipped, knowing her wish was about to be granted. 'Due to the nature of the film, which is intended to lift the nation's spirit, and the fact that it will highlight the work of the WAAF as well as the RAF, we've decided to grant the request.'

'Thank you, ma'am.' Jess could hardly quell the urge to jump up and down on the spot.

'You'll be released from Filter Room duties from Monday week.' Flight Officer Morgan gave Jess a stern glance. 'Don't make us regret the decision.'

'You won't, ma'am. I promise.'

Jess practically skipped back to the Filter Room just in time to join May and Evie as they lined up to show their passes.

'What was all that about?' Evie asked.

'Tell you later,' Jess said as she waved her pass at the guard and went inside. 'I've got to be on my best behaviour.'

She had thought she might find it hard to concentrate but there was an air of suppressed excitement in the Filter Room that temporarily drove out all thought of the film. The Controller briefed A Watch as they took their stations. 'We've had intelligence that something will be coming out of France today. We don't know any more than that, but we've assigned the code word, "Big Ben" to anything new.'

All senses tingling, Jess focused on her area of the table and made sure she was up to date with all the tracks and didn't miss anything new being placed. Was this to do with the new secret weapon Evie had mentioned on Jess's first day? She thought once of her aunt and Hannah then firmly put them out of her mind. She could best help them by doing her job.

Time stretched on. Jess was just combining two tracks – a glance at the sector clock told her it was 0745 hours

– when she was aware of a flurry of activity further down the table, centred around the plotter connected to Swingate RDF station. The plotter was speaking to a filterer who Jess only knew vaguely. Her eyes were open wide in alarm. Then the filterer stood on a chair. 'Big Ben, Big Ben, Big Ben!' she called. Immediately the Filter Room burst into an orderly uproar. The Controller rapped out a string of orders, resulting in several officers snatching up their telephone receivers. Everyone else in the room simultaneously continued with their own work while remaining fixated on the new plot. Jess shivered to see it was approaching at a greater speed than anything they had seen before, at an altitude far higher than a flying bomb. This was it, Jess knew. The secret weapon the Nazis had threatened. She wished she could follow what was happening, but she had her own tracks to focus on. She could only pray that whatever the weapon was, it didn't strike anywhere near Poplar.

Her watch ended not long afterwards. She was in a fever of worry as she left the Filter Room with Evie and May.

'Did either of you learn any more about Big Ben and where it hit?' When Evie and May shook their heads, Jess paced across the garden. 'I have to go to Poplar. Check on Vera and Hannah.'

Evie caught her arm. 'Wait. Be sensible. You can't go dashing off to Poplar every time anything comes near London. London's a huge place. The odds are, Vera and Hannah are perfectly safe and unaware of anything wrong. If you go tearing over there now, you'll only worry them.'

Jess drew a shaky breath. 'I know. You're right. I've just got a bad feeling about Vera and Hannah coming back to

London. It's so hard to relax when I know exactly how many flying bombs are headed that way every day.'

'Look. Come back to the mess with us and have breakfast. I'll ask the other filterers and see what they know.'

'But—'

'Then after breakfast, May and I will come with you to Poplar.'

'Good idea,' May said. 'I've been looking forward to meeting your family.'

Some of Jess's anxiety eased. 'You're both gems, do you know that?'

'Remember that when it's time to buy Christmas presents,' Evie said.

They still hadn't been able to learn anything new by the end of breakfast so, true to their word, Evie and May accompanied Jess to Stanmore underground station to make the journey to Poplar. The worst of the rush was over by this time, so when the empty train rattled into the station there were only a small number of people waiting to get on. The three friends found themselves alone in a carriage, giving Evie the opportunity to grab Jess's arm as they sat down. 'Remember, Jess, you can't breathe a word to your aunt about—' she glanced around the carriage even though they were obviously the only occupants '—Big Ben,' she finished in hushed tones.

Jess nodded. Now she had had time to calm down and think clearly, she knew Evie was right. She'd been all fired up to use this latest threat as a way of persuading Vera to take herself and Hannah back to the safety of Wales. Now she realised she could do no such thing. Everything she learnt in the Filter Room was top secret. However worried she was for her family's safety, she couldn't discuss it with anyone outside the Filter Room. 'Fat chance of getting Vera to change her mind about staying in London,' she said bitterly. 'Sometimes I really hate knowing what I know.'

Evie and May both nodded grimly.

'We do help people, though,' May said. 'Remember Milan. He would have drowned if not for you.'

'I suppose you're right,' Jess said, doing her best to ignore the stab of guilt when she thought of Milan.

'Of course she's right,' Evie put in. 'Milan and countless people are alive today because of us. And there are plenty of others like us, all working together to keep Britain safe. We can trust them to look after our loved ones if we can't be there for them.'

The train drew to a halt in the next station; more people got on, forcing Jess, Evie and May to change the subject.

'Oh, you'll never guess,' Jess said, bouncing on her seat as she remembered the events of the previous night, 'I forgot all about it after… well, you know. But something so exciting has happened.' She went on to explain about her taking a role in the film. 'I'm going to be in an actual film. Can you believe it?'

'It's nothing more than you deserve,' May said. 'You're going to be amazing.'

'I'm really happy for you,' Evie said. 'It'll help you get acting jobs after the war, too.'

'I know. It feels too good to be true.' She'd felt so left out the other day, with Evie and May looking forward not only to futures with Alex and Peter but with careers in mind as well. Now Jess could see a way back to the glamorous lifestyle she had aspired to when she'd been an actress.

She spared a fleeting thought for Milan. Would there be room for him in that life? In the end she decided not to think about it too closely. Milan had plans to return to Czechoslovakia and find his family, after all. Although she understood, she had no idea if he intended to return, and she couldn't ask. Not yet. Not when her feelings were so confused.

–

They changed from the Bakerloo line to the District line at Charing Cross and headed to the East End. When they emerged at Bromley station, Jess felt a twinge of nerves at the thought of Evie and May meeting Vera. Despite knowing Vera wouldn't dream of giving away her secret, she felt a vague dread that Evie and May would work it out somehow. How would they react if they found out what she had done?

It was a huge relief to turn into Farthing Lane and find no smoking crater where the houses should be.

'See,' Evie said, patting Jess's arm, 'I told you everything would be all right.'

Jess gave her a shaky smile. It could have been so different. They'd passed enough boarded up areas where houses had once stood for her to know everything could change in an instant. The street was empty of playing children this time. It took Jess a moment to work out why. 'Bother,' she said. 'Hannah will be at school. I quite forgot the schools will have gone back by now.' Of course, Hannah's schooling would be another argument against moving her again.

'How old is Hannah?' May asked.

'Five. She started school last year in Welshpool. I 'ope the little mite gets on with the kids here.'

They found Vera scrubbing her front step. She rose from her knees, wiping her soapy hands on her apron when Jess called her name and greeted Evie and May with a broad smile. 'I've 'eard so much about the two of you. It's lovely to meet you at last. Come in, come in. I'll make us a brew.'

Jess offered to help but Vera waved her away. 'Go on with you. It's just a pot of tea. I'm not so old I can't manage that.'

Jess went to sit in the front room with Evie and May, frustrated at the failure of her attempt to speak with Vera alone.

'This is a pretty room,' Evie said when Jess joined them. She was looking round at Uncle Jack's framed cigarette cards and the pale green wallpaper sprigged with daisies. She went to the fireplace and examined a framed photograph of Jess and Vera, taken when Jess had been celebrating her first small part in a play. Looking at the photograph now, Jess felt a wave of sadness at how badly she had let down the confident, optimistic girl she had been then. 'Have you always lived here?' Evie asked. 'You never speak much of your home.'

'Most of my life,' Jess replied. 'My mum died when I was six, and I never knew my dad. Auntie Vera and Uncle Jack were like parents to me. I was quite a handful. Bet they were relieved they couldn't have kids of their own.'

The moment the words were out of her mouth, an icy cold chill ran down her spine. Five painful seconds ticked out from the clock on the mantelpiece while she tried to think of a way to undo her terrible blunder. Think! 'I... ah, that is, they thought they couldn't, till Hannah arrived. Miracle baby.'

Thank heavens Auntie Vera chose that moment to walk into the room, china cups rattling on the tray. 'Let me take that, Auntie,' Jess said, springing forwards to relieve Vera of the heavy tray. She placed it on the low table beside Vera's armchair. 'I was just telling Evie about Hannah,' she said.

'Oh, yes. Our little miracle baby.' Vera, bless her, must have heard Jess's slip up. 'Well, not so much of a baby now,' Vera said, settling in her chair. 'I can hardly believe she's in her second year at the infants' school.'

'How's she getting on?' Jess asked, seizing the chance to steer the conversation away from Hannah's birth.

'She's loving it. So don't you go giving me any more grief about moving her back to the countryside, Jessica Josephine Jane Halloway.'

There was a stifled giggle from the depths of Evie's armchair. Jess shot her a glare before turning back to Vera. 'But—'

'No buts. You've 'ad your say, my girl, and I understand your worry. We went away during the Blitz, and listening to the stories, we missed a terrible time, even though this 'ouse wasn't 'it. Things are safer now, though. Everyone says the war's all over bar the shouting, and I'm not dragging the poor child back into the middle of nowhere just on your say-so.'

Jess subsided. She knew her aunt all too well. There would be no budging her now she had her heels dug in. Even if she was free to tell them about the new danger, it would make no difference.

Vera patted Jess's hand. 'I know you mean well, Jess, but we can't put our lives on hold for ever because we're afraid of what might happen. Hannah's doing well at school and making friends. She was being teased something terrible by the kids in Welshpool. Anyway, not even Wales is completely safe. Cardiff and Swansea both had attacks.'

'Welshpool's miles from there. Anyway, there have been no flying bomb strikes in Wales.' If Jess was free to reveal what she knew, she would have said that while she didn't know enough about the new weapon, it, like the flying bombs, had been aimed at London.

'Look,' Vera went on, 'the point I'm making is that if it's your time then it's your time, and there's nothing you can do about it. If there's a bomb out there with my name on it, I'd rather meet my end in my own 'ome. Anyway, I 'eard on the radio last night that the Battle of London is over. Our brave lads 'ave finally found a way of stopping those blasted Doodlebugs.'

In a move that signalled the subject was at an end, Vera picked up the teapot. 'Now let's 'ave a cuppa before the tea gets cold, and you can tell me your news.'

'Well, I suppose I 'ave got some really exciting news. I'm going to be in a film.'

'With Leonard Steele, can you imagine?' May put in, her eyes shining.

'Leonard Steele?' Vera gave Jess a sharp look. Jess tensed. She had never told Vera who Hannah's father was. Vera, however, had probably drawn her own conclusions at the time. Jess had to admit, she had been so giddy with infatuation for Leo at first, she might have mentioned him to her aunt and uncle rather a lot, just for the pleasure of speaking his name.

Vera pursed her lips and splashed milk into the cup, slopping more into the saucer than landed in the cup. 'Well, I suppose you know what you're doing. I thought you'd put all that acting business behind you.'

'I had. I mean, I *have*. This is nothing more than a fortnight's work. I'll be back on duty before you know it.'

'I hope so. You seemed so settled in the WAAF. Still—' Vera gave an approving smile at Evie and May '—your friends seem to have sensible heads on their shoulders. I dare say they'll keep you on the straight and narrow.'

'Don't worry, Mrs…' Evie trailed off, looking embarrassed. Jess realised she had never told Evie or May what Vera's surname was, having always spoken of her as Auntie Vera.

'It's Mrs Knight,' Vera supplied. 'But don't call me that. Mrs Knight is my mother-in-law.' Vera gave a theatrical shudder, even though Jess knew she got along well with Uncle Jack's mother. 'You can call me Auntie Vera like Jess here. I've always got room for a couple more nieces.'

'Auntie Vera,' May said, as though trying out the name. 'I like that. I never had an aunt.'

And the conversation moved on, away from the dangerous subject of Leonard Steele.

–

'I like your Auntie Vera,' May said when they emerged from Charing Cross station that evening. Vera had insisted upon feeding them lunch, and then they had wanted to stay to meet Hannah when she came home from school. The girls had managed to stave off their tiredness while with Vera and Hannah, but Evie had nearly nodded off on the ride from Bromley, so Jess had promised to buy them all a cup of coffee at the Lyons Corner House on the Strand to fortify them for the return journey to Stanmore.

'She's a brick, isn't she?' Jess said, striding out. 'I—'

A distant rumble made her stop mid-sentence. She could swear the ground had shaken. All around them, people had stopped in attitudes of alarm.

'What was that?' May said, clutching Evie's arm.

'It sounded like a bomb,' Evie said, looking worried. 'But why was there no air raid warning?'

Jess saw the understanding dawn in her friends' eyes as the same moment it struck her. She remembered the high speed of the 'Big Ben' that morning. There would have been no time to sound a warning for anything travelling at that speed.

All tiredness forgotten, they turned as one for the underground.

'There's bound to be someone in the mess who knows what's going on,' Jess said.

When they got back to Stanmore they made straight for No. 2 Mess and cornered a Filter Officer from B Watch, who had taken over from them that morning.

'The Big Ben?' Patricia North nodded. With a wave of the hand, she invited them to sit with her in a quiet corner of the anteroom. 'Yes, the Filter Room was in uproar for most of the morning.'

'Does anyone know what it is?' Jess said. 'Where did it hit?'

'Epping Forest. By all accounts, it's something like the flying bombs only much bigger. I've heard talk that there's been a second strike not long ago, but no one knows where.'

'I know. We felt it,' Jess said.

'I hope no one was hurt,' May said.

Evie looked grim. 'A blast that size, if it hit a populated area, there'd have been no escape.'

Chapter Ten

The news on the radio that evening was frustratingly quiet about the mysterious new weapons. Jess, Evie and May didn't learn more until they went back on watch the next morning. The Controller briefed them on the events of the previous day.

'The track we picked up yesterday was a new weapon called a V2. The first one hit Epping Forest and caused no fatalities. Sadly a second one struck Chiswick yesterday afternoon, killing three people and injuring many more.'

In the brief pause that followed, Jess exchanged glances with Evie and May. So that was what they had heard. Jess shuddered to think that distant roar had marked the deaths of three people. Three people who would have had no warning of their approaching end.

'As you will have gathered yesterday, these V2s travel at huge speeds. We estimate it takes only five minutes for them to travel from their launch points in France to London. As such, it is impossible to give any warning to the general population.' The Controller's face turned grave. 'It has therefore been decided not to make knowledge of V2s public. The prime minister is of the opinion that it would cause needless panic. We are confident that once the Allied Advance has cleared the Germans from Northern France, Britain will be out of range of these weapons. The threat, therefore, will be short-lived. I need not remind you that everything I have told you remains strictly secret.'

And so ended her last hope of persuading Vera to take herself and Hannah to safety, Jess reflected as she took her position. She had to finally concede that she would never be able to convince Vera to return to Wales. All she could do was pray a V2 never came their way.

–

What with her worries over the V2s and the excitement of her role in the film, Jess had completely forgotten about her next date with Milan, which they had arranged for that evening. Tired out as she was from lack of sleep the previous day, she would have sent Milan her excuses had she not wanted to give him the violin. The thought of his face when he saw it perked her up and gave her the energy to set out again with Evie that evening for the Abercorn Arms. May had pleaded tiredness, and Evie was only coming to the Abercorn to meet Alex; they had arranged to go to the cinema together. That left Jess alone with Milan. She wasn't sure if that was a good or a bad thing.

Milan was already at a table when she arrived. His eyes sparkled when he saw her, and he sprang to his feet before she could sit down. 'Remember the custom,' he said and kissed her on both cheeks.

The cheery greeting Jess had prepared flew from her mind. She didn't understand why a chaste kiss on the cheek should make her so flustered. 'How could I forget?' she said, gripping the handle of the violin case.

He put both hands on her shoulders, and his gaze softened. 'You grow more lovely every day.'

Flirting she could handle, but Milan's expression held only sincerity. Feeling suddenly uncertain, she swatted his hands away and sat down. 'Go on! Is that your way of sweet talking me into buying the drinks?'

'No. I got you a port and lemon,' he said, pointing to a glass she hadn't seen before, 'but if you—' His gaze fell on the violin case in Jess's hand and he swallowed, his eyes widening. He sank into his chair as though his knees had given way. 'Is that…?'

She nodded and passed it across the table to Milan. 'It's yours.'

Watching Milan's expression as he took the violin case in trembling hands was like watching a child reach for a much longed for Christmas present. Jess took a sip of her drink to ease the tightness in her throat then explained how she had come by the gift.

Milan touched one of the clasps then let his hand drop. 'It is truly for me?'

'Yes. Go on. Open it. I don't know if it's any good.'

Milan moved their drinks to another table then placed the case in front of him.

—

Jess looked uncharacteristically anxious. She must have mistaken his hesitation for reluctance. 'It will be perfect,' he assured her. He would have gladly accepted a child's violin at this stage.

He levered open the clasps and opened the lid, drawing a sharp breath of longing when he saw the instrument inside. This was no beginner's violin. He could almost hear the rich, mellow tones it would make. The strings were slack; it would take some tuning. He couldn't resist lifting it from its case. His left hand curled around the neck. It was as though the violin had been moulded to his hands. He lifted it to his chin then closed his eyes and took a deep breath. The scent of resin and polished wood took him back to the practice room in Charles University. The violin felt totally natural in his hands, and he found his fingers moving over the strings in silent arpeggios. It might be five years since he had held a violin, but his muscles still remembered how to play, and that gave him a spark of hope. When all the fighting was over, maybe he would be able to pursue his dream.

'Blimey, they should make handbags like this.' Jess's voice jerked him back to the present, and he opened his eyes. She was exploring all the pockets and compartments in the case. There was no trace of the sophisticated veneer she usually hid behind when she knew people were watching her. Instead she opened lids and ran her fingers over the velvet lining with a wide-eyed enthusiasm that was all Jess. This was the Jess he had wanted to see when he had made the clumsy comparison of her with ivy. Although his English was good enough for everyday communication, there were times he wished Jess could understand Czech. He would have far less difficulty explaining what was in his heart in his mother tongue.

She tugged at the piece of ribbon at the narrow end of the violin case, opening the lid of the little compartment there. She pulled out a duster that was wrapped around a circular object. 'What's this?' she asked, unwrapping it.

'Rosin.'

She prodded it with the tip of a finger. 'What's it for?'

'Coating the hair. To stop the bow from skidding across the strings.' He took the bow from its place in the lid and tightened the screw until the hair had the correct tension.

'Look.' He took the rosin from Jess and ran it up and down the bow, sending a flurry of fine powdered rosin drifting down upon the table. The fingers of his right hand took up the old familiar grip upon the ebony frog.

'Are you going to play something?'

He shook his head and reluctantly replaced the violin and bow in the case. 'It will need much tuning, and I need much practice.' He took in their surroundings. 'I think the landlord would throw me out if I tried tuning my violin in here.'

My violin. The enormity of those two simple words struck him. 'Thank you, Jess. You cannot know how much this means to me.' That she cared for him enough to find him this magnificent gift brought a lump to his throat. She had seen a violin in a shop window and thought of him. If they hadn't been in a crowded pub, he would have taken her in his arms and kissed her. As it was, her nearness as she leaned across the table, gazing at him with shining eyes sent a frisson of awareness across his flesh. A beguiling hint of floral perfume now competed with the scent of rosin.

A sudden thought struck him. 'You must let me pay. How much—?'

'It didn't cost a thing. I told you.'

Milan frowned. Jess had said something about where she had got it from, but he had been too overwhelmed to take it in. Something about a woman in an antiques shop. 'Then I must pay the woman who gave it to you.'

He half rose from his chair, but Jess placed a hand over his, sending prickles of electricity shooting up his arm. 'She won't accept any money. I tried. Anyway, her shop will be closed by now and I don't know where she lives. I think she would like to see you, though.'

Milan nodded. 'I will. I must thank her in person.'

The matter closed, he put away the violin and turned his attention to Jess. Now he came to look at her properly, he thought he detected shadows in her eyes as though she was worried about something. 'Are you well, Jess? You look tired.'

'Well that's a fine compliment to pay a girl.' For a moment he feared she would hide behind her façade again. Then she caught his eye and gave a small smile. 'I *am* tired, as a matter of fact. I thought I worked odd hours when I was an actress, but I'll never get used to the shifts here. It's getting that I never know if it'll be daylight or pitch darkness when I go outside every day.'

'Is that all?'

Her shoulders sagged. 'You don't want to hear all my worries.'

'Yes I do. If it's important to you, it's important to me.' She'd understood how much having a violin again would mean to him. Why couldn't she share her deeper feelings with him? It was frustrating that every time he seemed to get a step nearer, she would take two steps back.

'If you must know, I'm worried about my aunt. I went to see her the other day. Tried to persuade her to go back to Wales. With all the flying bombs and… suchlike, I can't sleep for worry. But she refuses to budge.'

Milan knew exactly what she meant by the 'suchlike'. He had been briefed about the V2s, knew that's what many of his reconnaissance missions had been about. 'I am sorry,' he said. 'I do understand why you are worried.' He tried to convey his full understanding through his tone. 'I wish I could help but there is nothing.'

Jess sighed. 'It helps that you understand.'

Then she sat up straighter. 'Anyway, now we've established there's absolutely nothing we can do, the best thing is to try and forget our worries for now.'

'Good plan. What do you suggest?'

Jess rose. 'First I'm going to get us each another drink, because I have news I want to celebrate.'

He kept his gaze fixed on her slender upright figure as she walked to the bar, admiring the swing of her hips. He wasn't alone in his admiration – Milan saw several heads swivel as she walked past. One man called something to her that Milan couldn't catch. Jess tossed her head and replied, 'You wish.'

When they had been at Amberton together, some of his friends had wondered at his bravery in pursuing a girl who so clearly enjoyed to flirt. Milan hadn't been worried, recognising her fierce loyalty for her two friends. It was one of the qualities he most admired in her. He knew that once her heart was given, she would be equally as loyal to the man she had given it to. It made him all the more determined to ensure that man was him.

Jess soon returned, placing another beer in front of him and holding a glass of something fizzy.

'Tell me what we are celebrating,' he said, raising his glass to her in thanks.

'You'll never guess what,' she said. 'They're making a film – a drama about the RAF – and they're filming some of the background shots and scenes at Bentley Priory.' In her excitement, her tiredness and worry faded from her face, leaving her glowing and animated. It was how he always liked to picture her when they were apart. It was how he had remembered her in the long years since her abrupt goodbye before leaving Amberton.

'A film?' He recalled her enthusiasm at organising the pantomime at Amberton. She would be in her element with film makers prowling the grounds of Bentley Priory. 'Who is in it? Anyone famous?'

'Leonard Steele.'

'Wow.' Milan didn't take much interest in films beside their music scores but even he had heard of Leonard Steele. 'Didn't he make that one about the pirates?'

Jess nodded. 'Wait till you've heard the good bit. They were filming some shots that I was in, and the director noticed me. I've been given permission to play a minor speaking role. What do you think?'

'That is wonderful.'

'It was Leo – Leonard Steele – who managed to wangle it, I think.'

There was something self-conscious about her expression when she mentioned Leonard Steele that set alarm bells ringing in Milan's head. Not to mention the familiar way she spoke of him. 'Leo?' he repeated.

'Oh, that's what everyone used to call him.' Jess looked him directly in the eye and gave a smile that seemed to say there was nothing to worry about. Milan wasn't fooled, though. There was the briefest flicker of discomfort that reminded Milan that Jess was a good actress. Most other women would be gazing at the floor at this point.

'You knew Leonard Steele before the war?' While Milan might not be as good an actor as Jess, he managed to make the enquiry sound casual. If he had met someone as famous as Leonard Steele, it would have been his conversation opener, not something he mentioned as if of no importance later on. Of course, Jess had been carrying the violin case when she arrived and had been excited about giving him his gift, so perhaps it wasn't so strange after all that Jess hadn't opened with her news.

'Oh, yes, I had a minor role in a West End play that he was starring in.'

'Yet you were friends?' Milan hated the way that made him sound. It made him seem like a jealous lover who needed to know about every man his girlfriend had met in the past. He wasn't like that at all. He trusted Jess; there was no way she would two-time him.

'He took an interest in the newer actors. Mentored us, you know.'

Milan nodded. That happened in the world of music as well – a more experienced performer nurturing the talent of a younger artist. 'It was kind of him to remember you.'

There it was again, a flicker of discomfort quickly disguised. 'Isn't it exciting, though?' Jess said. 'I just 'ope I can still remember 'ow to act. It's been years.'

'You will be... what is the expression? Top hat.' He refused to be jealous. He would show Jess that he could be encouraging and supportive, even if he was haunted by the thought of Jess mixing with a famous and handsome film star.

Jess grinned. 'I think you mean top hole. Thank you. It means the world to know you're behind me.'

See? There was nothing to fear. Anyway, even if Jess did admire the famous Leonard Steele, Milan would not give up easily. Leonard Steele was part of her past, but he would make sure he, Milan, was the only man in her future.

Her future. But didn't his plans for the future involve going home? Where did Jess fit in with that? Maybe it would be kinder to let her go.

He immediately dismissed the notion. Jess had worked her way into his heart, and he couldn't bear the thought of a future without her. Besides, the war wasn't over yet. It was something to worry about later.

Chapter Eleven

'Are you quite sure you know what you're doing, love?' The mug Vera was washing slipped out of her hands and fell into the sink, splashing soapy water down the front of her pinny. After several days of tracking more flying bombs and V2s, Jess had been anxious to see her aunt. Although by this time she knew Poplar hadn't been hit, she still needed to reassure herself all was well. Of course, that meant listening to Vera's concerns about Jess mixing with Leonard Steele again.

'It's a film role – I'd be mad to turn it down.'

Vera shook her head. 'I thought you'd left that life behind years ago.'

Jess knew what Vera was worried about, that she would be caught up by the excitement of it all and led astray. After all, she had gone astray quite spectacularly last time. 'It's time I started thinking about what I'm going to do after the war. I won't be in the WAAF for ever, you know.' Although the realisation came with a twinge of sadness. She had learned so much in the WAAF as well as made the best friends she had ever had. Yes, she had loved the glamour that clung to acting – nothing could quite match the thrill of being part of a stage production from first read-through to soaking up the applause of the audience and then the parties after the performance. She couldn't deny, however, that she didn't miss the feeling that she always had to push to get ahead. First there were the auditions that ended in disappointment, then watching other actors on stage, knowing she could be as good if not better if only someone would give her a chance. Then there was the joy of her first roles, only for the exhilaration to fade as she set her sights on larger roles, and always there was the seemingly impossible dream of reaching top billing. Something she had been about to grasp when her stupid mistake had torn the dream away.

Her heart swelling at the memory of how Vera had supported her through the very worst of times, Jess kissed Vera's cheek. 'I won't let the glamour turn my head again, Auntie. You can be sure of that. Once bitten, twice shy.' She grabbed a tea towel and started to dry the dishes.

Faint worry lines still creased Vera's brow, however. 'I agree you should give some thought to your future. Isn't there some skill you could use that you've learnt in the WAAF? Surely with you doing clerical work, you could land yourself a nice job as a secretary.'

Even if Jess had been free to explain what her work really involved, she didn't have the heart to disabuse her aunt. 'Maybe. I'll think about it.' Think about how desperate she would need to be before choosing to do a boring desk job. The prospect of being at the beck and call of some pompous businessman when she had been an officer in the WAAF made her feel physically sick.

She must have been convincing, though, for the lines on Vera's brow eased. 'I know you won't do anything rash. You're a good girl, and I'm so proud of the way you've turned your life around. You're too sensible to throw it all away. Now, tell me all about this part you've got.'

'It's only small. It'll be fun to get a taste of the life of a film actress, though.'

'Have you seen the script yet?'

'Yes, I got it yesterday. It all looks… fine.' If truth be told, Jess was a little disappointed. Not with the size of her role – in fact she had a more prominent role than she'd been led to believe at first. No, it was the character she was playing.

Vera was watching her with arched brows. Jess gave in. She could never keep a secret from her aunt. 'Oh, all right. You've seen through me. My character is a complete drip.' Her character was also a WAAF officer, but that was where the similarity between Fiona Loveday and herself ended. Fiona did an unspecified job that seemed to involve nothing but sitting at a desk outside the Station Commander's office and making the occasional phone call. Her main role in the film seemed to be as the love interest of Squadron Leader Charlie Fleet – Leo's character. Jess had read the script in disgust, knowing the writer had no idea what WAAFs really did.

'You won't believe this, but in one scene my character gets so frightened at approaching enemy bombers that she faints dead away into the hero's arms. I mean, who actually does that?'

'No woman I know,' Vera said, looking grim.

'Definitely no one I know.' Remembering her own experiences of the Battle of Britain, of how the quiet, shy May had helped everyone out when they had been trapped in a shelter during a bombing raid, how Evie had calmly carried on with her work when she had known Alex was fighting for his life in the air, Jess felt nothing but rage at the way WAAFs were being depicted.

'You could tell them you won't do it,' Vera said, looking hopeful.

'If I refuse now, especially after all the trouble they've gone through to get me released from duty, I can say goodbye to ever getting another acting job.' If anything, this made Vera look even more hopeful, forcing Jess to add, 'Look. I'm not saying I want to go back into acting, but I need to keep my options open. There will be a lot of people looking for work at the same time when all this is over, so I can't afford to pass up any opportunities.'

'So you're going to go along with this… this soppy Susie character?'

'Her name's actually Fiona Loveday, but Soppy Susie is much better. I'll refer to her as that from now on.' Jess laughed, feeling better already. 'But no, I won't go along with it. I just need to find a way to change the character without getting a reputation as a difficult actress.'

'How are you going to do that?'

'No idea, but I'll come up with something.'

It was time she brought Evie and May in. Together they were bound to think of a way to stop this travesty.

–

Filming started the next day, and as both Evie and May had been out with Alex and Peter the previous day, Jess didn't get a chance to speak to them. She therefore arrived on location at Bentley Priory with no idea how to change her character's storyline.

A woman with a clipboard met her when she arrived at the area of the grounds cordoned off for the film makers. 'Jess Halloway?' The woman consulted her clipboard. 'You're to go to hair and makeup first.' She pointed at a group of khaki tents pitched at the far end of the area.

Jess strode off in that direction, filled with the same mix of nerves and eager anticipation that she associated with her first day in the WAAF. There were several people milling around near the tents, and as she approached she looked for Leo, seeking out a familiar face. At first she couldn't find him, but then she spotted him talking to a tall, portly man in the centre of the cordoned off area. A small crew was nearby, in the process of setting up cameras, sound equipment and lighting. The sight set her insides aflutter as it hit her that today could be her one chance to prove herself as an actress. A wooden sign hung over the entrance to the first tent proclaiming it to be the hair and makeup station. She pulled aside the canvas flap serving as a door and went in. A bank of chairs, trestle tables and mirrors lined one of the long sides of the tent. Pots of makeup, combs and brushes were arranged on each table. A plump middle-aged woman in a pretty sage green dress greeted her. 'You've arrived in good time, I see. Oh, but you're already in costume.'

Jess looked down at her uniform. 'It's not really a costume. I'm a WAAF so I was told to come in uniform.'

The woman looked her up and down. 'It's a good cut. Much better than anything you'd have got if you'd relied on the costume department.'

'Thank you.' Jess smoothed down her skirt, thankful for every penny she'd spent at the tailors on Savile Row to get the perfect fit. A well-fitting uniform hadn't featured in her reasons for applying for a commission, but the day she had stood in front of the mirror at the tailors in a made-to-measure uniform had been one of the best days of her career. 'If I'd known we'd get an allowance for a tailored uniform, I'd have gone for officer training much sooner,' she'd said to Evie and May the next time she'd seen them. She was all the more grateful for her tailored uniform now she was to be filmed in it.

'Take a seat.' The woman ushered her to a chair. 'I'm Flora, by the way.'

'Nice to meet you, Flora. I'm Jess.'

'Oh, I've heard all about you,' Flora said, eyes twinkling. 'I was doing Mr Steele's makeup earlier, and he told me to take good care of you.'

'That was kind of him.'

'Oh, he's got a heart of gold, that man. Always time for a chat with the likes of me and the cooks. Always a kind word.'

It was this consideration that Jess had been attracted to when she had first begun rehearsing *All Manor of Murder*. He had gone out of his way to be kind to the people who worked backstage. Of course, they had, in return, often seen to it that Leo got the best treatment, often falling over themselves to run errands for him even when it meant neglecting other members of the cast.

Flora draped Jess with an overall to protect her uniform then took off her cap and started removing the hairpins holding Jess's hair in the smart style she had adopted. 'You've got me for both hair and makeup,' Flora said. 'Budgets are tight and film crew are more scarce.' Her tone was apologetic.

Jess hurried to reassure her. 'It's a real treat to have someone do my hair and makeup at all. When I was on the stage before the war, I had to do my own.'

'Well, let's see about your hair.' Flora brushed it out, encouraging it to fall in glossy waves down to Jess's shoulder blades.

'Aren't there any other actors in for hair and makeup this morning?' Jess asked. She had been looking forward to the gossip that could always be had when being made up.

'Not this time. It's just you and Mr Steele in the scene they're filming today.'

'Only one scene?' Jess pulled her script from her pocket and unfolded it in her lap. 'It doesn't look very long.'

'Ah, this is film. Very different from stage acting. It can take all day – days, even – before the director gets the scene exactly as he wants it. And you're filming outdoors, too, so you might act it perfectly but have to do a retake because the light wasn't right.'

'I can see I've got a lot to learn.' It was already strange to be filming out of order. Today's scene was about two thirds of the way through the story. Jess was used to stage acting where performances were done in order. Today Jess was going to have to try to act angry about Charlie standing her up on their last date, something that had happened in a scene she hadn't performed yet. It was an odd way of doing things, to her mind, although she was sure she would get used to it.

'You'll do well enough,' Flora said. 'You've certainly got the looks for the part. I'd have killed for hair like this when I was younger. There. That's perfect. I'll need to give it another brush through before each take, but that's all it will need.'

'Aren't you going to put it up?' Jess looked at herself in the mirror. Flora must have magic in her fingers because Jess's hair billowed in thick shiny waves – a look that would make many a Hollywood actress green with envy. It was, however, against regulations. Her CO would have a fit if she could see her now. 'It won't look right under my cap like that.'

'Oh, you won't be wearing the cap. It's too official looking. You need a softer look. More romantic.'

Jess knew there was no point in arguing. Flora was, after all, only following the art director's instructions. She sat back in her chair to let Flora do her makeup. Flora chattered as she worked, and soon Jess was up to date on all the personalities in the production.

'What's Allan Ford like?' Jess asked, naming the director. He had a reputation of being a hard taskmaster, and she'd been nervous about working for him.

'I'll let you into a secret,' Flora replied, lowering her voice even though there was no one else in the tent. 'He may want people to think he's a crusty old slave driver with a heart of stone, but that's all for show. He knows what he wants, mind you, and will work you hard until he gets it, but beneath the harsh exterior he's got a heart of gold. If you can show him you're keen to learn and want to work hard, he'll be putty in your hands.'

Jess stored up this information, knowing that the relationship with her director could make or break an actress's experience.

'There. All ready for Mr Steele to sweep you off your feet.'

Jess looked at her reflection. Like the hair, her makeup gave her a veneer of glamour only usually seen on a Hollywood actress. While she considered herself skilled at applying makeup, she had never managed the polished look Flora had given her. 'I can see why all the best productions use you,' she told Flora. She gave an experimental smile, admiring how the deep red lipstick made her teeth look even whiter than usual. 'This looks amazing.'

'Well, I had a good canvas to start with,' Flora said. 'You should see the state of some of the actors I have to make up, especially after a hard night's partying. Without makeup they would look more like characters in a horror film.'

Jess laughed. She rose, allowing Flora to help her off with the protective drape. 'I should hire you as my personal makeup artist. I could do with you the day after a night watch.'

Being with Flora had helped calm her nerves, but they returned in full force when she went to join Leo.

Allan Ford was with him and took over with no time for niceties. 'Let's see what you're made of then.'

Together with Leo and the director of photography, they began by blocking the scene. This involved walking Jess and Leo through the scene, showing them the markers placed where they should be standing at each point. There was little time for her to assimilate all that information before she had to rehearse the full scene with Leo. To her relief, the level of concentration required in the Filter Room helped her remember everything with more ease than anticipated, and it was Leo who made mistakes in the first couple of run-throughs.

'Sorry,' Leo said to the director after the second mistake. 'Jess didn't quite turn in time, and it distracted me.'

Jess opened her mouth to protest then thought better of it. While she thought she had followed instructions to the letter, it was more likely that she'd made a mistake than an experienced film actor like Leo.

The scene itself was very short. In it, Fiona, Jess's character, was to walk through the grounds and change direction to avoid Charlie, Leo's character, when she caught sight of him. Leo then had to run to catch her up. The remainder of the scene was Leo trying to explain that he had been unable to meet her the evening before because duty had unexpectedly called him away. Jess had trouble with Fiona's anger at Leo. If Fiona had been a civilian it might have been different, but Jess couldn't imagine a WAAF not understanding that if a pilot was ordered on a mission, he had no choice but to obey.

Still, it didn't seem appropriate to argue over the script so early on in the filming, so she followed direction to the letter.

'Don't you miss playing to an audience?' Jess asked Leo as they sat down between takes. Flora stood behind Jess, brushing out her hair again, which had lost some of its wave in the light breeze. She was finding filming a strange experience. It had taken all morning, but the director had pronounced himself happy with the takes they had done of the argument scene, so after lunch – a spread of sandwiches arranged in another tent – they had moved on to film a scene from near the start of the story. This was the scene where Charlie first sees Fiona. After spending the whole morning being angry, it felt odd to switch to be starry-eyed at her first sight of the handsome pilot.

'Who needs an audience when you have the finest crew any actor could ask for?' Leo turned to grin at Flora. 'Isn't that right, Flora?' Then in a stage whisper to Jess that Flora was clearly meant to hear he added, 'Flora's the best in the business. Treat her right and you'll look like a goddess.'

Jess couldn't see Flora's face but she could guess it was wreathed in smiles as she replied, 'Ooh, you are a one, Mr Steele.'

After applying a little more powder to Jess's face, Flora left them.

Leo immediately turned to Jess and said in a lower voice, 'Not that you need makeup to look like a goddess.

Come out with us tonight? A group of us are going to a club in Town. It'll be a chance to meet the other actors.'

Jess, tired from hours of standing around, wanted nothing more than to curl up in a comfy armchair in the anteroom and chat over the day's events with Evie and May. However, she wanted to make a good impression, and it seemed stand-offish to refuse to meet the rest of the cast.

By the end of the day, her back and feet ached, and she wished she could think of an excuse not to head into London. Still, she had enjoyed herself, and the excitement of being on a film set hadn't faded. Her nerves had eased with each take, and she had even earned a grudging nod of approval from Allan Ford. Coming from him, it had felt like winning an Oscar. If she wanted to act after the war, she was heading in the right direction.

—

'How did your first day of filming go?' This question was directed at Jess by Maurice Michaels, an actor in his late fifties whose bushy moustache waggled impressively with each word. Jess gazed at the moustache, mesmerised. Maurice was playing the Station Commander. Jess was familiar with his work, as he had played several authority figures in other films she had seen. They were due to play several scenes together when they returned to the studio, so Jess had been glad to meet him.

Jess, her eyes and throat smarting from the smoke filling the club, cleared her throat and raised her voice to be heard over the band, which had just launched into an energetic number. 'It's been interesting. There's so much to learn.'

Leo, who had been talking to the director, now addressed Maurice. 'She's a star in the making, I tell you.'

This was the first time he had commented on her work, and it gave her a flutter of pleasure.

'Then I look forward to working with you in a few days.' Maurice then turned to a younger man on his other side – Jess recognised him as an up-and-coming actor who had been released from the RAF Film Unit to make this film. Leo returned to his conversation, leaving Jess stranded between them. The music was too loud to carry on a conversation with those sitting across the table from her, so she drank her drink and tapped out the rhythm of the tune on her glass with her fingers.

Milan wouldn't have ignored her. When she went out with Milan, even when they were in a crowded room, he gave her his full attention. Again, she had the uncomfortable feeling she was being disloyal to Milan by coming here, which was ridiculous. Milan never objected to her socialising with others, and it wasn't as if she had any romantic designs towards Leo.

After what felt like an age, Leo turned towards her. He seemed to look at something over her shoulder for a moment, then he held out his hand. 'Forgive me for ignoring you,' he said. 'It was terribly rude of me, but I wanted to discuss tomorrow's scene with Allan.'

Jess relaxed, ignoring a tiny voice in her mind that wanted her to ask him why she couldn't have been included, seeing as she was in the scene as well. 'That's all right. I was enjoying the music.'

Leo's hand was still held out to her. 'Would you like to dance?'

Glad of something to do, she took his hand and allowed him to steer her onto the dance floor. There was no denying Leo was a skilful dancer. He wove expertly around the other couples, spinning and dipping her until she felt like Ginger Rogers to Leo's Fred Astaire. She couldn't help but be aware of the stir of interest surrounding them. Gradually, the other dancers moved off the dance floor and lined the perimeter, watching. Jess's heart thrilled at the attention she was getting. A flash of light made her blink. An instant later she realised a photographer stood at the edge of the dance floor, pointing a camera at them. Jess shot him her brightest smile. Suddenly the evening didn't seem so dreary. This was the life she had dreamed of before the war. Who would have thought a chance meeting could bring that dream back within her grasp?

When the dance ended, everyone applauded, and Jess revelled in it, her weariness forgotten. This was why actors coveted film roles. A mystique clung to film actors, and they were the centre of attention wherever they went. Everyone knew who they were. People were interested in Jess simply because she was with Leo. Imagine the awe they would regard her with had they seen her in films.

They returned to their table. However, before Jess could sit down, Leo glanced at his watch. 'I don't know about you, but I need my beauty sleep if I'm to be up bright and early tomorrow.' Jess was thirsty and could have done with another drink. However, a glance at her watch showed her that she really ought to get back if she was to be fresh for the next day's filming.

As they were about to leave the club, Jess saw that the photographer she had seen earlier was now standing beside the door. He took another picture, then a second man Jess hadn't noticed before stepped in front of them. 'Mr Steele, would you care to introduce our readers to your lovely companion?'

It dawned on her that the photographer must be from a newspaper. Still, it wouldn't do any harm to be photographed. Once again, feeling as though she was in her childhood dream, she raised her chin and gave the men her best smile.

'This is Jess Halloway. Or, I should say, Section Officer Halloway. She is a very talented actress who has agreed to play my leading lady in my latest film, *Knights of the Skies*.'

It took all of Jess's self-command not to shoot Leo a look of amazement. Although she played Leo's love interest in the film, her part was minor. She could by no stretch of the imagination be described as a leading lady.

The reporter was scribbling down her name. Then he asked, 'Your leading lady off screen as well? Having watched you dance together I have to ask.'

Jess drew breath, on the verge of telling the man to mind his own business. She shut her mouth when Leo squeezed her arm. 'Now, Arnold, you don't expect me to give up all my secrets, do you?'

As far as Jess was concerned, it was a most inadequate answer. She turned her head as Leo steered them out of the door, intending to set the record straight. Leo fixed a smile on his face and murmured in her ear. 'Don't say a word. This is priceless publicity.' Before she knew it, they were out on the dark street.

Chapter Twelve

Thankfully the next evening, Leo wasn't so insistent about Jess coming out with him, which was a relief. She hadn't seen Evie or May since she'd started filming and she longed to catch up with them. Footsore and aching from hours of standing around waiting for the right light, she staggered back to No. 2 Mess and flung herself into an armchair in the anteroom and ordered a cup of tea.

'Have a good evening last night, ma'am?' the waitress asked when she brought the tea.

Jess was flummoxed. 'What would you know about it?'

The girl coloured. 'I… oh, nothing really, ma'am.' She made her escape.

Jess was too tired to pursue the matter. Probably just gossip about the film, she supposed, as she kicked off her shoes and put her feet up on the ottoman with a sigh. She closed her eyes while she waited for her tea to cool.

'There she is.'

Jess opened her eyes to see Evie and May standing over her. 'I was waiting for you,' she told them. 'You're not going on watch, are you?'

Evie snorted. 'Only two days on set and you've already lost track of the watches.' She lowered herself into an armchair with a groan and dropped a folded newspaper onto her lap. 'Got off at 1600 hours. May dragged me for a walk on the common. Why she thought that was better than a cup of tea in here I'll never know.'

'I get such awful backache hunched over the table,' May said, sitting beside Evie. 'I needed a walk to work out the kinks.'

'You could have stayed a driver. Spent your days sat in the driving seat.'

'Except all the times I had to change the spark plugs or wheels,' May said. 'I prefer what I'm doing now. I like using my brain.'

'Anyway, we're getting off the point.' Evie threw the newspaper to Jess. 'Care to explain this?'

Jess picked it up, 'It looks like a newspaper,' she said, pretending to examine it. 'You read it to learn the news around the world.'

Evie snatched the paper out of Jess's hands and hit her over the head with it.

'Hey, mind my hair.' Jess carded her fingers through it, trying to restore the waves that Evie's attack must have flattened. 'It took ages for the hair and makeup lady to get it looking right.'

'As to that, make sure you put it up before dinner or you'll get a dressing down from the CO. But that can wait.' Evie opened the newspaper. 'What we're both dying to know is how did you manage to get so cosy with Leonard Steele?' She handed the newspaper back to Jess, pointing to a picture.

Jess took it, a suspicion of the truth forming. A glance at the page confirmed her worst fears. There were two photographs – one of her dancing with Leo and another of them leaving the club. In both she was giving a dreamy smile as though completely infatuated. The headline was splashed across the top of the page in bold letters: 'A leading lady for Leonard Steele.'

'I don't believe it,' Jess said. 'I never thought it would get into a national paper.' She hadn't been thinking at all, she realised with a rush of shame. She had been so carried away with the glamour of being photographed on Leonard Steele's arm, she hadn't given a single thought to the consequences.

'Is it true, though?' May asked. 'Are you and Leonard Steele courting?'

'Course not.' Jess flung the paper to the floor, picture side down so she couldn't see her infatuated smile. 'The only reason I went out was to meet the whole cast. Those two photographs were practically the only time I was actually alone with 'im.'

'How did the reporter know you would be there?' Evie asked. She picked up the paper and read the article.

'No idea. Maybe he hangs out at likely clubs hoping to spot someone famous. Or he just happened to be there for an evening out. The club wasn't far from Fleet Street.'

'So he took his photographer with him, complete with camera, for a drink after work?' Evie shook her head. 'Someone told him Leonard Steele would be there.'

'Then it was someone on the cast hoping for a bit of publicity. I told you, everyone was there.' Jess laughed. 'I'll have to look out for anyone who looks disgruntled tomorrow. It's backfired on them, seeing as the reporter was only interested in Leo.'

'And you. If you want to return to acting, this would help.'

Jess hadn't looked at it that way. 'I suppose. I wish the camera hadn't caught me looking so soppy, though. It looks like I'm head over heels.' Her conscience pricked her. While she might not be in love with Leo, she had been bedazzled by the glitz – at least, she had when Leo had started to pay her attention on the dance floor. She preferred to forget the majority of the evening when he had ignored her in favour of the director.

Then another thought struck her. 'Oh no. What if Milan sees this?'

Evie regarded Jess, head tilted to the side, with a gaze that made Jess squirm. 'I thought you and Milan were just friends. Would it matter if he saw it?'

'Oh, all right. I admit it. I feel for Milan more than just friendship. There. Are you satisfied?'

Evie gave a slow smile. 'That wasn't too hard, was it? If it took a photo of you and Leonard Steele to make you see sense, then perhaps it's not such a bad thing after all.'

'It is if Milan sees it and thinks I'm—' Jess read out the first line of the article, her nose wrinkled in disgust '—that special lady who has finally tamed notorious bachelor, Leonard Steele.' She read a bit further. 'Gawd 'elp me. I've been promoted to Squadron Officer.'

Evie snatched the paper and scanned the article, choking when she found the part Jess had just read. 'Two ranks in two days. That's fast work, even for you.'

'It's not funny. The senior officers are going to think I'm getting too big for my boots.'

'No they won't,' May said. 'If you go to the CO first and explain the mistake, I'm sure she'll understand. The press are always getting things wrong.'

'I suppose you're right.' Although Jess didn't relish the prospect of going to the CO cap in hand. 'That doesn't solve what to do about Milan, though.'

'Why would Milan not understand if you tell him the truth?'

Jess leaned over to give May a hug. 'May, just because you landed yourself the dearest, sweetest natured man in the air force, it doesn't mean every other man is exactly like him.' Thank goodness. Although Jess was very fond of Peter, she couldn't imagine getting any thrill from dating him.

'You make him sound like a fish! I didn't *land* him.'

'Sorry, poor choice of words. I should have said, you bowled him over with your courage, intelligence and beauty.'

The old May would have blushed fiery red and denied it. Jess was proud of her friend that she could now take compliments without objecting, even if she did still blush. 'Anyway,' May said, 'we're supposed to be talking about Milan and you. Don't deflect the conversation to me and Peter. Milan might be nothing like Peter, but he's crazy about you. He's not going to run a mile just because you were photographed dancing with another man.'

'Especially not after that violin you gave him,' Evie added. 'He knows he means more to you than someone to flirt with. Give him some credit for understanding you.'

Jess sighed, remembering how Milan had seemed to see right through her when he'd accused her of hiding her true self beneath the sparkle. 'Maybe there are some things I'd rather he didn't find out.'

Evie frowned. 'What do you mean by that?'

Jess bit her lip. She had meant her comment to sound light-hearted, but it had come out sounding all too serious. 'Oh, I would hate him to find out how long it takes me to do my face and hair,' she joked. 'I want him to think this is my natural look.'

The others laughed and the moment passed. Jess turned the conversation to another problem on her mind. She couldn't dismiss her fears of being found out so easily, though. She couldn't bear her friends to think differently about her, which they surely would if they found out that she was Hannah's mother and had been lying to them all these years.

'What shall I do about this script?' she asked, pulling the pages from her inside pocket.

'What's wrong with it?' Evie asked. 'I thought you were loving being a film actor.'

'I am.' Her tone rang hollow, shocking her. 'I mean, I am.' She managed to put more feeling into it this time. 'I just hate the character I have to play. She's such a drip. I mustn't complain, though. It's an amazing opportunity.'

May plucked the script from her hands. 'What makes her a drip?'

'She doesn't act or think for herself. Her only function in the plot seems to be to moon over the hero. Look.' She leaned forward and opened the script. 'The scene I played yesterday was the one place where Fiona – that's my character – has a disagreement with Charlie – Leo's character. Yet by the end of the scene, Leo has talked her round to his point of view and she's all happy again.'

May looked at the script, frowning. 'Mind if I read the whole thing?'

'Help yourself. As long as you give it back in time for me to learn tomorrow's lines.'

May curled up in her armchair and buried herself in the script.

Jess stretched and rose. 'Ah well, I suppose I'd better go and make myself respectable for dinner. Either of you coming to the pub later?'

May didn't answer, lost in the script. Evie shook her head and said, 'I'm going out with Alex later.'

142

Jess went upstairs to her room fighting off that feeling of being left out.

–

May cornered Jess after dinner. Evie had already left by this time, and Jess was reluctantly coming round to the fact that she would have to stay in and learn her lines.

'I don't think Fiona is a complete drip,' May said as she handed the script back to Jess. 'It's all a matter of interpretation.'

'What do you mean?'

'Well, look at the scene you filmed yesterday. You could take it to mean that Fiona's being unreasonable because Charlie couldn't possibly have abandoned his squadron to meet Fiona.'

'How else could you take it? No WAAF would fail to understand that duty has to come first.'

'But she's in love. Every time she sees him could be the last. She's trying to hide her fear from Charlie, trying to be brave for his sake, but in that scene all those bottled-up feelings burst out. Taken in isolation, that scene makes her look petulant but put it together with the rest, if you play it right, Fiona becomes a rounded character who's trying to hold it together and hide her doubts and fears from Charlie because she doesn't want to spoil the precious moments they get together.'

'I suppose… wait. What do you mean if I play it right?'

May looked down. 'It's… well, it's up to you. How you act her scenes. You could take it at face value and play her like a drip. Or you could say exactly the same words and show that inner fight.'

It was like looking at one of those optical illusions where the same drawing could look like two different things depending on how you looked at it. 'May, you're a genius.' She paused as a thought struck. 'Only...'

'Only what?'

'What if the director doesn't like how I play it?'

May put her hands on her hips in an eerie imitation of Auntie Vera. 'Jessica Jane Josephine Halloway, I can't believe what I'm hearing.'

'It's Jessica Josephine Jane, actually.' Jess grinned despite herself. 'What can't you believe?'

'That you of all people are afraid to stand up to a man.'

'I'm not.' Jess's voice rose with indignation. Somehow being accused of cowardice by her most timid friend stung more than if the accusation had come from Evie. Although if she was honest with herself, she couldn't deny there was truth in what May said. 'Maybe you're right. I just don't want to get a reputation of being difficult to work with. I'd never get another acting job.'

'How does trying to make it the best possible story turn you into a difficult actress?'

Jess didn't know. She just knew that actresses who spoke up for themselves usually didn't get invited back to audition for any other parts.

May was giving her a penetrating stare that made Jess squirm. 'You want to know what I think?'

'I'm not sure. I'm starting to regret encouraging you to speak up for yourself.'

'I think you're afraid to dig too deep into Fiona's emotions because it might force you to admit you're in love.'

'I... what? I'm not in love with Leo.' Jess felt a stab of panic. Had she said or done anything that let slip how she had felt for him in the past?

'Not Leo. Milan.'

'Oh.' Jess's relief was short-lived, however. She really didn't want to put her feelings for Milan under the spotlight.

'Think about it,' May said. She glanced at her watch. 'You'd better get a move on if you're going to learn your words for tomorrow.'

Jess nodded. She knew how hard May found it to speak her mind. Only the deepest conviction that she was right would have made May say what she had. Somehow that made it hit home far harder than if Evie had been the one to speak up. Even now, May was biting her lip, looking as though she wished she'd held her tongue.

'Thank you, May,' she said. 'I will think about it, I promise.' Then, because she wanted to show May how much she appreciated their friendship she added, 'Have you got time to hear me read through later? If I'm going to try persuading the director your way's best, I need to be sure I've got my performance spot-on.'

After four years of close friendship, perhaps it was time to open up more to her friends.

–

'Hold it!' The director strode onto the set, interrupting the scene rehearsal, and addressed Jess. 'What was that?'

With a sinking heart, Jess rose from behind the desk. The film crew had finished filming the exterior scenes and now they were in the studio. The set they were filming in today was the antechamber to the station commander's office, where Jess's character had her desk. As she faced the director, she wished they were still filming outside. If things went badly, she couldn't run away from the set.

She squared her shoulders. 'I thought it made more sense of the scene we filmed on Monday if we see here how afraid Fiona is of losing her heart to a man who could be dead before the day's end.'

Following May's suggestion, she had spoken the words exactly as they appeared in the script. Instead of gazing dreamily into Charlie's eyes, however, she had turned away abruptly before Charlie could cup her face. She should, she now realised, have warned Leo what she was going to do, because the sudden move had thrown him, leaving him off balance. She braced herself for a tirade.

'You thought you'd change the whole dynamic of a scene without consulting me?' Allan Ford's face screwed into a scowl. He thrust out a hand towards his assistant and clicked his fingers. The assistant must have been a mind reader, for she scurried forward and placed the script into his outstretched hand.

Jess's heart beat a rapid tattoo against her ribs while Allan perused the script.

Eventually he looked up. 'Think you know better than me or the writer how Fiona would feel?'

'I know exactly how it feels.'

Allan's eyebrows twitched together, and he looked her up and down as though reminded that her uniform was no costume but the one she wore by right. 'What do you think, Leo? Can you make it work playing the scene her way?'

'I suppose I could give it a go.'

'Very well. We'll do one run-through your way then go back to mine. The final decision rests with me.'

'Thanks for your wholehearted support,' Jess muttered to Leo as they retook their places.

'It doesn't do to have both of us in Allan's bad books. This way, I can speak up for you later if necessary.'

Jess supposed there was some merit in what he said. She couldn't help thinking that Milan would have championed her had he been in the same position.

To give him his due, Leo played his part perfectly. Jess threw herself into the role. While she waited for the crew to reset the stage, she thought of Milan and how she felt knowing the risks he took each time he flew into enemy territory. She had replied to Allan without thinking, and she guessed her raw honesty was what had persuaded him to give her way a try. She usually tried to push her fears for Milan into the back of her mind. Now she allowed them to occupy her thoughts. She was seeing him tomorrow. Would it be the last time she saw him? Would he even still be alive tomorrow?

By the time the crew were ready for another run-through, she was in the same barely-suppressed emotional state she imagined Fiona would be in.

Chapter Thirteen

Jess flew into No. 2 Mess at the end of the long day and made straight for May, who was writing a letter at one of the tables in the anteroom. She grasped May by the wrists and despite the considerable difference in height, raised her from her seat and whirled her around. 'You genius, May. It worked!'

She swung May in circles until they were both weak from laughter and forced to collapse in chairs to recover. The other women in the anteroom looked on, giggling.

'Care to enlighten me?' It was Evie who spoke. Jess peered up to see her standing over them, her lips twitching.

'I think it means she managed to persuade the film director that WAAFs aren't complete airheads who only exist to swoon over the pilots.' May pulled a handkerchief from her pocket to wipe her streaming eyes. She looked at Jess. 'Go on. Tell us how it happened.'

'Yes, I want to hear this.' Evie dropped into a neighbouring armchair and regarded Jess expectantly.

Jess pulled herself upright in her chair with a groan, putting a hand to her aching stomach muscles. 'Well, I could have thought through my approach better. I nearly ended up getting the chop.' She filled her friends in on her disastrous first attempt at acting the scene and the director's grudging concession to let her play the scene once her way. 'Over lunch, the director went into a huddle with the writer, and when they came back, he said he'd decided to play the character my way.' She looked at May. '*Your* way. As I said – you're a genius. Honestly, they should employ you as scriptwriter. Give you a credit, at least.'

'No way.' May clapped a hand to her chest. 'Promise me you won't say anything.' She looked so horrified, Jess had to bite back a laugh. 'Anyway, it's more a matter of interpretation than writing.'

'Keep your hair on. Your secret's safe with me. Anyway, wait until you hear the best bit.' It took all Jess's self-control not to bounce in her chair. 'The director said he wants to completely rewrite Fiona's part, make her role bigger.'

'That's amazing,' Evie said, then she frowned. 'Wait. Won't that take longer to film? I thought you'd only been released for a fortnight.'

'Yeah.' This was the part Jess wasn't so thrilled about, remembering Laura Morgan's reluctance to lose a Filterer Officer for even two weeks. 'I told Allan – the director – that the WAAF won't be happy, so he's going to make the request personally.' She grimaced. 'I dread to think what the CO's going to say.'

'You want to do it, though, don't you?' May asked.

'You bet. This is the chance of a lifetime. There is one thing, though.' Jess glanced around the anteroom. By this time it was filling up, as it was only half an hour until dinner. She gave a little shake of the head. 'Not here.' She rose. 'Come on. I need to do my hair before dinner.'

When they were up in the bedroom, Jess brushed out her hair and watched Evie and May in the mirror. 'I know we're not supposed to talk about what goes on in the Filter Room outside its walls but—'

Evie stopped her with a raised hand. 'I know what you're going to ask. I promise you, we're keeping an eye out for your aunt. There's nothing for you to worry about.'

Jess relaxed, assured that Evie would have said if any V2s or flying bombs had hit Poplar. 'You're both stars. I never thought I would worry so, being out of the Filter Room. Never realised I would miss knowing what's going on.' She put down her hairbrush and started to pin her hair into regulation off the collar rolls. 'In a strange sort of way, when I'm there I feel like I'm watching out for them. Ridiculous, I know, when there's nothing I can do, but that's how I feel.'

'I know what you mean,' Evie said. 'I must say I'm glad my mum is safe in Oxford.'

'And my dad is safe in one of His Majesty's prisons,' May said with a grin.

'So both me and May can watch out for your aunt and cousin while you're away.'

Jess hastily wiped away a tear before it could smudge her mascara. 'Did I ever tell you you're the best friends a girl can have?'

'Yes, but we don't mind hearing it again,' Evie said. 'You can tell us about it over dinner.'

'It's a deal, although I've got to go out again afterwards. Leo invited me to join him for a drink.'

In the mirror, Jess saw Evie and May exchange glances. 'You've been seeing a lot of Leo,' Evie said, her tone a study of neutrality.

'Honestly, I'd almost think Auntie Vera paid you two to keep an eye on me. It's just a drink. Nothing more.'

'What does Milan think? Has he seen that newspaper article?'

A cold hand seemed to squeeze her heart; the feeling she got every time she thought of Milan seeing the photos of her and Leo together. 'I don't know. I haven't seen him for a while.'

'He's a lovely man, Jess. I'd hate to see him hurt.'

'I won't 'urt 'im,' Jess said, sticking pins into her hair with such a savage motion that she jabbed her scalp. 'There's nothing going on with me and Leo. You don't know 'ow it is in this business. The pressure to mix with the right people, to be seen to be successful so you're in the running when they're casting the next picture.' And although Jess wouldn't admit it, the glamour of the past few days had been a powerful lure. Wartime Britain was such a dark, dreary place. Was it so wrong to grab hold of a night or two of sparkle and resplendence when offered?

'Jess.' Evie stood behind Jess and put her hands on her shoulders in a conciliatory gesture. 'No one's accusing you of anything. We don't blame you for enjoying yourself while you can.'

Jess released a breath. 'Sorry. I don't know why I'm so touchy.'

She rolled another strand of hair and was about to pin it above her temple when she remembered her decision to be more honest with her friends. She dropped her hands to her sides, leaving the lock to unravel against her cheek. 'All right, maybe I do. I suppose you struck a nerve. Truth be told, I feel guilty about seeing so much of Leo.' Before Evie could ask why she continued to see him, Jess hurried on. 'I'd much rather be with Milan.'

She faltered when she took in Evie's expression. It was a look she had come to know. It meant Evie was piecing together everything Jess had said and mentally applying logic to each statement. Jess braced herself.

'I understand why you want to mix with the film people,' Evie said. 'But why go everywhere with Leo? You're a cast member. You don't have to go as his date.'

Jess flung the last of the hair pins on the table and spun around. 'You don't understand. I—'

May held up a hand, her expression of hurt bewilderment enough to silence Jess. 'Why so defensive? We're on your side.'

Yes, and she wanted to keep it that way. While the sensible part of her trusted them not to reject her, the part of her that had locked away the secret for so long held back. It wasn't easy to let go when she had been on her guard for so long. Still, Evie and May were her friends. Surely she could tell them some of the truth, even if not the whole of it.

'I'm sorry,' she said again. 'I'm not being fair to you. If you must know...' She fiddled with a button on her jacket as she tried to decide how much to reveal. 'Well, I knew Leo before the war. We went out for a while.'

If she had told them she'd once been a lion tamer she didn't think they could have looked more stunned.

'Wait. Leonard Steele?' May's voice was several tones higher than usual. 'You went out with Leonard Steele?'

'And never told us?' Evie stared at Jess as though seeing her for the first time.

'Look, I'm ashamed of the way I behaved back then. That's why I kept quiet about it. When I first met Leo, I'd just landed my first good part, and he was playing the lead in the same play. He took me under his wing.' Jess swallowed, hating having to relive her stupidity. 'I was flattered by his attention.' She snorted. 'More than flattered. I let the excitement go to my head and let go of what little sense I had. He mixed with a really wild crowd, and I went everywhere with him.'

It was why she had decided not to tell him when she got pregnant. At the time, Leo had been involved with a group of socialites who drank, gambled for high stakes and, Jess suspected, even took cocaine. She didn't know if he still led that lifestyle, but it wasn't one she wanted Hannah mixed up in. Jess had never been offered cocaine herself but a few times she had seen Leo accept a twist of paper from a friend then disappear for a short while. When he reappeared, he'd displayed a strange energy bordering on aggression that had made Jess uncomfortable.

'I… well, I drank far more than I should have, and when I… woke up to what I was doing, was so ashamed.'

'The main thing,' said Evie, 'is that you stopped. It's in the past. I know the person you are now, and that's who I'm friends with.' There was nothing but concern and acceptance in her eyes – no condemnation. Some of the weight of dread on Jess's heart eased.

May nodded. 'We all make mistakes.'

Jess's mistake had been bigger than they knew. Nevertheless, it was a relief to have shared something of her past and receive only love and understanding in return.

She slipped in between Evie and May and took their arms, her vision blurred from tears. 'You're the most wonderful people in the world. Do you know that?'

'As are you,' Evie said in a voice that brooked no argument. 'Now come on, or we'll miss supper.'

Jess hastily finished arranging her hair, her heart pounding. Dare she tell them the rest? Would Evie and May be so accepting if they knew the whole truth? She was slowly coming round to the belief that they would. Yet fear still kept her silent. Maybe they wouldn't reject her – she couldn't believe such true friends would ever cast her off for a mistake made in the past – but would they ever look at her in the same way again? What if they stopped teasing her for being a flirt and instead tried to change her behaviour? She couldn't bear to lose their wholehearted regard.

As for Leo, was she making the same mistakes again? Not that she wanted to resume their relationship, but was she getting carried away by the lure of show business? When she had first got the film role, it had seemed the perfect way to help her acting career after the war. Now she wondered if she wanted to act. If she did, socialising with Leo would bring her into contact with influential people in the business, yet it was a dangerous path to tread. She had stumbled before. Could she walk it safely this time, or would she fall?

–

Jess turned up her collar at the chill wind as she waited for Milan. She paced up and down in front of the gates to Bentley Manor, wondering if she should wait inside. Earlier in the month it had been unseasonably warm for October. Now, however, there was a distinct nip to the air. Still, it would help her stay awake. It had been a hectic few weeks, and she was finding the life of a film actress to be every bit as exhausting as working in the Filter Room.

To her relief, Laura Morgan had granted her extra leave from the Filter Room to finish filming. Although, true to Jess's prediction, she had not been pleased at first, she had unbent when Jess had explained the extended role would portray the WAAFs in a better light. 'Make us proud,' she had said with a smile before dismissing Jess.

Now Jess wondered if she would have felt so light-hearted at being allowed to carry on filming if she'd known how busy she would be. Long hours in the studio meant few free evenings, none of which had coincided with any of Milan's. Tonight would be the first time she had seen him since those ghastly photos had appeared in the paper. Milan hadn't mentioned it in any of his phone calls, so she could only hope he hadn't seen.

She rolled her shoulders and yawned. Despite her good intentions, she had stayed out late the previous night. Leo had taken her to a nightclub, where he had introduced her to several well-known people in the film industry and also his agent.

His agent had given her an approving nod then turned to Leo. 'Glad to see you're paying heed to advice for a change.'

Jess briefly wondered what advice Leo's agent meant. The next moment it flew from her mind when Leo introduced Jess to an actress so famous it had taken all her self-control not to squeal with excitement. When the woman turned away with a gracious smile and a wish for Jess's success in the film, Jess looked for Leo, bursting to thank him for the introduction to one of her heroines. It took a moment to see him, huddled in a shadowy corner, deep in earnest conversation with his agent. Guessing he had important business he wanted to discuss, Jess hung back. However, Leo must have noticed she was alone and murmured something to his agent, obviously to end the conversation. His agent clapped Leo on the shoulder, and Jess overheard him say something like, 'Trust me, it's in the bag.'

After that, Leo had spent the whole evening in her company. She had been so flattered by his attention, she had agreed to stay on far later than her good sense would have allowed.

Now, however, she wished she'd had an earlier night. Her eyes felt heavy as she looked down the road, seeking Milan by the golden glow of the setting sun. She wished her brain was less fuzzy from lack of sleep. Should she bring up the subject of the photographs herself? She couldn't make up her mind.

Then Jess's heart gave a little flutter when she saw him walking up the road from Stanmore. It felt good to slip her arm through his. There was none of the giddy excitement of seeing heads turn as she walked through London on Leo's arm, but there was a sense of homecoming, nonetheless. This feeling of contentment made her reluctant to bring up the subject of the photograph. She wouldn't mention it. Milan probably hadn't seen it, so why tell him about something that might upset him?

Then she noticed he was carrying the violin case. 'You don't want to return it, do you?' she asked, squeezing his arm.

'I have been practising,' he replied. 'To play for you. If you wish to hear, of course.'

'I'd love to.' Jess put more enthusiasm in her reply than she felt. She would have preferred to go somewhere where they could dance. She had never forgotten dancing with Milan at Amberton and longed to relive the experience. 'Where can we go?'

'The Rose and Crown. That is why I am late – I went there first. The landlord said there is a back room we can use.'

'Where do you practise at Benson?' Jess couldn't imagine his fellow officers being keen on hearing endless scales.

'In a hangar. The aeroplanes cannot complain.' He chuckled softly. 'Although I gave the station cat a nasty fright.' He spent the rest of the short walk to the pub describing how his playing had sent the cat fleeing from its hiding place on a Spitfire's wing, its fur standing on end.

Jess laughed along with him, relaxing, sure his good humour meant he hadn't seen the photographs.

When they reached the Rose and Crown, Milan bought drinks and collected a key from the landlord which unlocked a room at the back of the pub. It was clearly used as a storeroom now, with several crates of bottled soft drinks stacked against one wall. Half-buried behind a jumble of battered tables and chairs was a small raised platform that must have served as a stage when this room had been used for functions. An old upright piano stood beside one wall, together with a couple of metal music stands, knotted in an angular embrace.

'What do you think?' Milan gestured around the room.

Jess brushed the dust from a chair and sat down. 'It's not exactly the Savoy.'

'Wait until I start playing. My violin will transform the room into a glittering ballroom.' He removed the violin from its case and plucked a string, which made a distinctly unmelodious twang. 'Once it is tuned.'

Laughing, Jess watched him tighten the bow and apply a coating of rosin. Then he eased back the piano lid, dislodging an avalanche of dust that danced and glittered in the light from the bare light bulb dangling from the ceiling.

Milan played a note on the piano then bent over the violin, tuning the strings. Although he seemed absorbed in his task, every now and then he would glance up, catch Jess's eye. Again Jess got the impression he wanted to say something; whatever it was, he couldn't seem to find the words. Jess hoped it wasn't about the photograph.

She had just reached the conclusion that she ought to broach the subject herself when Milan gave a satisfied nod. He rose, placed the violin under his chin and ran through a series of arpeggios, his fingers moving faster than her eyes could follow. Then he looked at her, eyebrows raised. 'I will play you a Czech polka. It is called "Škoda lásky."'

He began a jaunty tune that set her foot tapping. At first she let the tune wash over her; she found herself entranced by the nimble skip of his long fingers across the violin's neck, the deft way they teased a vibrato tone from any note that was sustained for more than a beat. Then there was the way he held the bow. His fingers seemed to hover over the ebony grip, barely touching it. The bow didn't saw the strings as much as float above them, sweeping across the violin, drawing out a tune that managed to be both jolly and plaintive.

Something nudged at her consciousness, though it took a while to work out that the tune was familiar. 'I know this. It's not Shkoda… thingy. It's "Roll Out the Barrel."'

'Ah, but before it was "Roll Out the Barrel", it was a Czech polka called "Škoda lásky."' He drew out the second word like a sigh.

'I never knew that. What does it mean?' She tried to copy the sounds of the name. 'Shkoda lahsky?'

Milan placed the violin and bow onto the piano stool with great care. Then he looked directly at her, his intense blue eyes searching her face. 'I don't know exactly how to translate it.' A pucker appeared between his brows, and Jess had to fight the urge to smooth it with her fingers.

'It is something like the shame of love. No. Wasted love. Love that gives pain.'

Jess swallowed, wanting to look away. She couldn't seem to move. She certainly couldn't speak.

'The song is about love that has no return.'

Jess found her voice, although the words came out as little more than a whisper. 'Unrequited love?' She cleared her throat and dragged her gaze from his, forcing a smile. 'I think I prefer the English lyrics. Why don't you play something else?'

'I saw the photograph in the paper.' Milan's voice was gentle.

Maybe if he had shown anger, she would have hastened to excuse herself, tell him it meant nothing. As it was she was frozen, unable to drag her gaze from his face. Part of her knew she should reach out to him, reassure him. The other part feared to so much as blink in case it shattered the moment and destroyed them for ever.

'I know photographs can lie,' Milan went on in the same gentle voice, unaccusing. 'If you tell me it is not true, I will believe you. In return, all I ask is that you tell me if I waste my time with you.'

Now would be the perfect time for Jess the Flirt to make an appearance. That Jess would laugh off the photograph and make Milan feel like he was the only man in the world. That Jess would defuse the tension and she would be able to breathe again. That Jess was nowhere to be found.

'I don't know, I wish I did.' Why wouldn't he look away? Maybe then it would break this strange hold he had over her. Break the spell that meant she could only tell the truth. 'I don't want to hurt you, but I'm so confused.'

For some reason, her words seemed to cheer Milan. His lips curved in a faint smile. 'That I can work with. You are being honest. That is all I ask. In time you will see you are too good for Leonard Steele.'

She nodded. If only she could tell him the whole truth, that *Milan* was too good for *her*.

Milan picked up his violin again, all the tension gone from his posture. 'Now, I will play again, and you will tell me if I am ready to play for Mrs Swift.'

As the music washed over her – beautiful music that could wring tears from cold stone – Jess wondered yet again why Milan saw qualities in her she was sure didn't exist. It made her wish she possessed them. It made her wish Milan had known her before she had thrown her life away over a tawdry affair.

Later, as Milan walked her back to No. 2 Mess, Jess reflected that yet again Milan had not given her what she would consider a proper date – dancing or fine dining. Yet there had been a magic to the evening, listening to Milan play music that one moment made her want to dance, the next cry. It was an evening she knew she would carry in her heart for the rest of her life.

They walked in silence, Jess still painfully aware of all that remained unsaid between them. Her head and heart were too full for speech, though, and maybe Milan felt the same way for he escorted her back to Bentley Manor without a word. A heavy dread fell on her. Maybe Milan would decide it was too much bother to pursue her, that he couldn't face the pain of seeing her publicly linked with Leo. He had spoken of the pain of love, after all.

It hit her then with full force that she couldn't bear to lose him. She didn't feel anything for Leo any more.

They had reached the gates of Bentley Manor by this time. Suddenly afraid that he would leave without a word, that she would never see him again, she clutched his arm. 'Those photographs… they make it look like there is more going on between me and Leo than there actually is.'

'You don't have to explain yourself to me.'

'Yes I do. I want you to understand.'

'Perhaps I understand better than you think.'

It was quite dark by this time. She could only see Milan as a dark shape against the sky where he blotted out the starlight, and the faint glimmer of reflected moonlight in his eyes.

'Go on then. Explain.' As soon as the words were out of her mouth she quailed. He did, after all, seem to have an uncanny ability to see into her soul. She braced herself.

'I know that you see in Leonard Steele a life you thought was lost to you. Whether it is the man or the fame you are attracted to, only you can tell.'

'I don't love Leo.'

A brief silence. Then: 'So it is the fame.'

She couldn't bear his disapproval; nor could she say that she loved him. The words stuck in her throat, held back by the knowledge of her shame. She responded the only way she knew how. She gave a light laugh. 'You've found me out. I can never resist a bit of sparkle. You can't blame me for making the most of my moment of fame before I go back to being a boring old WAAF.'

'You are never boring.'

'Glad to hear it. Anyway,' she went on before Milan could say anything that might make her uncomfortable, 'it's been a lovely evening. I'm sure Mrs Swift would like to hear you play. Shall I ask her?'

As soon as they'd agreed on a day, Jess fled inside. Neither Evie nor May were there, and Jess was glad for the chance to sit quietly and think things through without interruption. What was the name of the first tune Milan had played? He had said it was about unrequited love. At the time, she had thought it was a declaration of love. However, now it came to her that he hadn't told her outright that he loved her. He had just been speaking of the song. She had been so busy trying to work out her own feelings from the jumble of attraction, guilt and unworthiness she felt when she was around him that she hadn't noticed that Milan had never spoken of love, either.

He seemed to know a lot about her. Maybe he already sensed she wasn't good enough for him.

–

Milan couldn't get Jess's worry from his mind as he flew over France the next day. Slowly the signs of the Allied advance gave way to areas where the Germans still clung on. His tension increased as it always did when flying over enemy territory. The Germans might be falling back, but he was well within range of the Luftwaffe should he be seen. He kept a constant watch for enemy aircraft and also looked behind him to ensure he wasn't leaving a vapour trail.

It was depressing, seeing the lack of progress made by the Allies. As ever when he saw signs of enemy troops below, his thoughts returned to Eliška and Franta. He had dreamed of home again last night, and now the pangs of homesickness were sharper than ever. Would his dream of a happy reunion come true, or would he return to Roztoky to find his family gone? While he knew it was only a matter of time before Czechoslovakia was freed, would it be soon enough for his sister and nephew?

He tried to push his worries from his mind as he flew on. He had been sent to photograph a possible V2 launch site. When Jess had told him about her fears for her family, he knew it was a V2 strike she feared, even though she had been unable to speak about it. While he could do nothing for his own family, it was good to know the work he was doing would potentially help Jess's.

He was approaching his target now. All he could see of the ground was woods and fields. Not that he would be able to spot launch sites from this height; all he could do was take the photographs and rely on the experts at RAF Medmenham to interpret them correctly. Once he arrived back at RAF Benson, the ground crew would remove the film magazines before he'd even climbed out of the cockpit. By the time he was in the briefing room for his mission debrief, the films would be well on their way to the developing and processing unit. Speed was of the essence if Intelligence was to get the information from his photographs in time to act on them, especially if they showed trucks carrying mobile launchers which could quickly be moved to a new location.

Another glance around the skies showed he was, thankfully, alone. Holding his breath, he banked and turned the cameras on, exhaling a sigh of relief when he completed his run with still no sign of enemy aircraft. As Jiří would say, this had been a milk run. All he had to do now was calculate his return course and head straight for RAF Benson. With luck, if the photographs revealed a launch site, the V2s could be destroyed before they were launched at London.

He thought again of Jess's aunt and cousin. Somehow, having names and personalities made his mission more personal. Perhaps flying reconnaissance missions weren't such a waste of time. While he had been furious at his transfer, he was starting to see how vital his missions were to the war effort, even if he wasn't fighting Nazis himself any more.

He was over the Channel now, losing height the closer he came to the English coast. He let himself relax, knowing himself out of range of most enemy fighter patrols.

It took an explosion off his port wing to bring his attention back to sharp focus. He stared out, craning his neck to look this way and that. Had he made a navigational error? Had he somehow ended up flying over the wrong coast? But no – he could see the unmistakable towers of the Chain Home station at Rye below him. A sudden calm washed over him – it must be anti-aircraft fire. He banked sharply, checking that his IFF transmitter was on. He had switched it off while over enemy territory because many pilots believed the signal it emitted could now be intercepted by German radar. It was definitely on, so why were the idiots aiming at him? The signal should tell them he was a friendly fighter even if they couldn't see the RAF roundels on his Spitfire.

Another explosion rocked his plane. What the hell was that? Fighting to regain control, he looked for the source. No anti-aircraft fire was that powerful.

That's when he saw it: a small cigar-shaped aircraft with blunt wings that looked like they had had their tips chopped off. It flew at high speed inland. He had seen enough images to know this was a flying bomb. The explosion must have been another flying bomb being struck by ack-ack. This one, however, was now out of range of the bursts of anti-aircraft fire and was streaking right towards London. He, however, had the height and speed to catch it.

He didn't even think, he just dived towards the bomb. He navigated an intercept course that would bring him below the bomb. Once in position, he glanced up, dry mouthed at the madness he was about to attempt. He'd heard other pilots describe how to knock a flying bomb off course, but he'd never tried it himself. One false step and the flying bomb would explode, taking him with it. The dark shape blotted the light from above. He had only one chance. With aching care, he eased the control column back, gaining just a tiny bit of height. The shape filling the canopy grew larger. Now he could pick out every rivet holding the sheets of grey metal together. With minute movements of his feet on the rudder, he positioned his plane so that his starboard wingtip was below the flying bomb's port wing. Holding his breath, he banked to 'nudge' the bomb's wing. He hit the wing tip then banked sharply to avoid a full collision. Craning his neck, he searched the sky for the bomb. He let out a ragged breath when he saw the bomb streaking out to sea. A moment later it plunged into the water, exploding in a column of mist.

Weak with relief, he checked his compass and resumed his course. Jess might never know, but he had done it for her.

Chapter Fourteen

It was another fortnight before Jess was able to see Milan again. Filming had finally finished, and she looked forward to returning to the routine of the Filter Room. She had been told that she would be needed later on to record her voice parts and possibly to film any additional scenes the writer decided to add. However, it had been agreed that Jess could fit this around her duties. They were somewhat short-handed in the Filter Room at the moment, with a group of the most experienced Filter Plotters and Filterers having been mysteriously moved elsewhere.

Evie had been on leave at the time, visiting her mother who had been taken ill with appendicitis. On her return, once her mother was on the mend, she had told Jess and May that she'd been glad to be away and so missed being transferred. She hadn't wanted to be separated from Jess, May and Alex for what could be months. No one spoke of the missing officers, but Jess privately believed they had been transferred to the continent. This was confirmed a few days later when information on V2 launch sites began to be reported to the Filter Room. They weren't allowed to speak of it, but Jess guessed the women were using V2 trajectories to locate where they were being launched from. Whatever they were doing, Jess could only pray their plan succeeded and as many V2s could be destroyed before launch as possible.

'A shilling for your thoughts,' Milan said as they walked through the dark streets. At Jess's snort of laughter, he said, 'That is what the English say, is it not?'

'Nearly. The English would only offer me a penny. You must value my thoughts more highly.'

'Either that or I expect more for my shilling.'

Jess sighed then gripped Milan's arm when she stumbled over an uneven paving slab. 'I'm afraid you won't get any new thoughts for your money. Still the same worries about my family. It will be good to be back on duty, though.'

'When do you start?'

'Tomorrow morning. I know I can't make any difference to what's happening, but I'll feel better being able to watch over them.'

'You made a difference to me.'

Jess gave his arm a squeeze. 'I'm glad I was there for you.' Then she remembered something Evie had told her. 'Speaking of keeping watch on you, what's this I hear about you flipping a flying bomb?'

'How do you know that?'

'I wasn't certain until now. An observer on the ground watched the whole thing and reported it. He had a good view of your plane's markings, enough to know it was from your squadron. Somehow, I had a feeling it was you. It sounded like the mad, reckless kind of thing you would do.'

'I didn't do it for the thrill. I did it for you.'

'For me?' They had reached the door to Stoneleigh and Swift by this time. Jess made no move to knock at the door, however. She gazed into Milan's shadowy face, straining to see his expression by the dim moonlight.

'I knew how worried you were for your family. I could not let the bomb through. Maybe it would have landed on your family's house.'

'But you took a terrible risk.' She could not comprehend how Milan had put his life on the line for her sake. Leo, for all the help he could give her acting career, would never risk his life for her or her family.

'So I should have watched it fly all the way to London?'

'No. Of course not. I just—' she swallowed, her heart thudding painfully. 'I mean...' For goodness' sake. She had never had any trouble speaking her mind before. Why was she finding it so hard now? 'You do know I would care if you got yourself killed, don't you?'

'I do. I think I have known it longer than you.'

Jess laughed, more to release the sudden tension than because she found his remark funny. 'Have you any idea how arrogant you can be?'

Without waiting for an answer, she knocked at the door. Stoneleigh and Swift would be closed by now, but when she had arranged the meeting Kathleen had told her she would be working in the shop all evening.

There came the sound of a lock turning and bolts being drawn, then the door opened a crack. 'Do come in,' came Kathleen's voice from within. 'Take care of the blackout curtain.'

They squeezed through the door and after a brief tangle with the heavy curtain, they were inside. Jess blinked in the sudden light.

'Come in, come in,' Kathleen said, leading them to a table and chairs she had arranged in the middle of the shop. The room looked less crowded than before, and Jess suspected Kathleen had cleared a space especially for Milan to play. 'I've put the kettle on and made some cake.'

She turned to Milan with a small smile. Jess saw that she looked much better than she had when she had given Jess the violin; the circles under her eyes were less pronounced, and her cheeks had regained some colour. While her hair was still pinned into a severe bun, there was a shine to the light brown hair that hadn't been there before. 'You must be Jess's young man. I can't tell you how much it means to me to know someone is playing my Danny's violin.'

Milan shook her offered hand. 'I can't tell you how much it means to have a violin again. I am Milan Mašek, by the way.'

'I'm so sorry. I should have introduced you.' Jess shrugged off her greatcoat and hung it on a coat stand. 'Let me make the tea while the two of you get acquainted.'

When she returned from the back room bearing a heavy tray holding teapot, cups, milk, plates and a huge carrot cake giving off a spicy aroma that set her stomach rumbling, Milan and Kathleen were both stooped over the violin case which Milan had placed on a chair.

'Oh, thank you, my dear,' Kathleen said, taking the tray from Jess and placing it on the table. 'You must eat first. I wouldn't have you think I invited you all the way here just to hear you play.'

As they munched on the delicious cake, however, it was clear from the glances both Milan and Kathleen directed at the violin that they both itched for Milan to play. Jess had to bite back a laugh at the eagerness with which Milan seized the bow when she collected the cups and plates to carry them back to the other room. When she returned, he was applying rosin to the bow. A piano stood against one of the walls, and Kathleen opened the lid and played him an A to assist him in tuning.

Once Milan had finished tuning, he turned to Kathleen with a look of apology. 'I went a long time without playing. I am still… how do you English put it – rusty? I hope I do not disappoint.'

Mrs Swift patted his arm. 'I'm sure you won't. Just seeing the care you're taking with my Danny's violin is good enough for me.'

Milan inclined his head towards Mrs Swift then said, 'I will play you a traditional Moravian folk tune to warm up.'

'As long as it's not "Roll Out the Barrel", or whatever you call it,' Jess said.

Milan gave a crooked smile. 'Not that one. I shouldn't say this as a Czech – from the part of Czechoslovakia you would call Bohemia – but I prefer Moravian folk music.'

He lifted the violin to his chin and started to play. The music was jaunty yet played in a key that also gave it a haunting air. Jess found her feet tapping even while she watched his face. Although he didn't close his eyes, his gaze seemed fixed on a point at a great distance from the antiques shop. Every emotion wrung from the strings could be read on his face, although while Jess had always thought it was the music that caused the emotion, she could have sworn this time the emotion led to the music.

When the tune came to an end with one single note fading into silence, neither Jess nor Kathleen spoke for a moment. Kathleen was dabbing at her eyes with a handkerchief.

'Wonderful,' she said at last. 'You're definitely not rusty.'

'I am, believe me,' Milan replied. 'I could almost hear my old violin tutor telling me off as I was playing.'

'Well, I thought it was perfect,' Kathleen said, tucking her hanky into her cardigan sleeve. 'I know I did the right thing in giving you Danny's violin. He would be happy to know his violin was being put to such good use.'

'What shall I play next?' Milan tilted his head towards the violin case. 'I found some music that your son must have been studying. I have been playing it and it is lovely, but I don't want to play something that would upset you.'

'Oh no, I would love to hear what he was working on.'

Milan drew a sheaf of music from the case. 'This is "The Lark Ascending" by Vaughan Williams. I have performed this before, so I already know the piece well. It is an orchestral piece, though. It really needs an accompaniment.'

'Oh, I can do that.' Kathleen's face lit in an eager smile. 'I used to play for Danny sometimes.'

Milan handed her the music and she sat at the piano, propping the music on the stand. After a moment's hesitation, she put her fingers to the keys and played the opening notes. Then Milan raised his violin and began to play.

From the very start, Jess finally recognised Milan's full talent. The opening, trilling notes evoked a lark soaring and swooping through the summer sky so clearly that she could almost imagine she was in open fields listening to the lark's joyful song. She felt a surge of sorrow that the war had ripped Milan so cruelly not just from his country and family but also from his chosen career. Would he ever find the success that he deserved?

She found herself watching Milan's fingers running up and down the neck of the violin, sometimes moving faster than her eyes could follow, at other times one long arched finger quivering upon the same string while the bow drew out a long vibrato note.

'That was beautiful,' Kathleen said, pulling out her handkerchief again. She suddenly gazed at her reflection in a mirror mounted upon the wall. 'Oh dear, I must look a fright.'

'Not at all,' said Jess, who thought Kathleen had more animation than she'd ever seen.

'You know, my Danny used to compare the different kinds of flying to different birds. He used to say bombers were like geese, flying in formation straight as an arrow to their destination. He—' Kathleen dabbed her eyes again '—he used to say that while a few geese might drop out, the formation always reached its destination.'

Jess felt a lump in her throat, thinking of the nights in the Filter Room, tracking the returning bombers, anxiously counting those who arrived in the main mass and waiting for the stragglers, praying everyone would return this time. 'What about the fighters?' she asked, her voice hoarse.

'Sometimes he said they were like hawks, hovering over a flock of smaller birds, waiting to strike. But at other times he compared them to larks, flying free, flinging themselves up in the sky without a care in the world.'

—

Jess was still thinking about this comparison after they'd left Mrs Swift, replete with tea and cake, and walking back towards No. 2 Mess. 'If bombers are geese and fighters are hawks or larks, what are reconnaissance pilots?'

'Eagles,' Milan replied without a pause. 'They fly high in the sky looking at the ground.'

'What do you prefer?'

Before he could answer, the sound of running feet approaching made them stop. Then they saw the dim circles of two shielded torches upon the pavement and heard a voice say, 'It's down here somewhere.'

'Evie?' Jess called.

The footsteps stopped. 'Jess?' The dim outlines of two figures appeared, one much taller than the other. Evie stepped closer. 'Jess, thank God. We were looking for you.'

'Why?' Jess asked. There was a long pause, and it occurred to Jess that Evie and May must have come here straight from standing watch in the Filter Room. Only the most urgent news would make them do that. Suddenly Jess wanted to run away, somewhere far away where she couldn't hear what Evie was so reluctant to say. If she didn't know, it wouldn't be true.

'Jess,' Evie said again, and now Jess could hear the tremble in her voice. She clutched Milan's arm.

'Just tell me.' Jess forced the words through frozen lips.

'You need to go to your aunt's,' Evie said. 'You know we can't say anything, but… well, you need to go.'

Chapter Fifteen

If Milan hadn't put a supporting hand around her waist, Jess thought her legs would have given way. An icy chill gnawed her insides and her ears buzzed, muffling what Milan, Evie and May were saying.

Then Milan's voice cut through the confusion. 'I will drive you. I borrowed my CO's car this evening.'

Jess nodded. She wasn't about to question how Milan had wangled the use of a car for a non-essential journey.

'We'll come too,' May said.

By this time they were striding down the street. Jess had no idea what direction they were headed in, she just clung to Milan's arm and allowed him to guide her. She had to run to keep pace with his long, swift strides.

'There is no room. The car is only a two-seater.'

The words flew over Jess's head, and she felt unable to grasp what they were saying. The question she wanted to ask hammered in her head: V2 or flying bomb? She couldn't ask, though, knew Evie and May couldn't tell what they had learned while on duty. Gradually her thoughts cleared. Surely if it had been a flying bomb, the sirens would have sounded, whereas V2s were too fast for the air raid warnings to be any use.

A V2, then. She felt sick. If a V2 had struck Jack and Vera's house, there would have been no escape.

She struggled against a wild desire to scream. It was only her years of WAAF training that enabled her to force the fear to the back of her mind. Until she had proof, she refused to believe her aunt, uncle and Hannah had been harmed. Hannah. The thought of her daughter's bright, beautiful face made her stagger as though she had been struck.

Milan steadied her. 'Why not wait at the Mess?' he said. 'I will take Evie or May and send word.'

'No.' Jess drew a gulping breath to steady herself. 'I'd go mad, waiting. I 'ave to come with you. I 'ave to know.'

Evie put a hand on her arm. 'We'll wait up. Send word if you need us.'

Jess clutched Evie's hand in silent thanks then allowed Milan to sweep her off to his car.

-

There was no need for torches. Flickering orange light lit their way from several streets away. While Jess knew there was no way Evie and May could know the exact place the V2 had struck, they must have known it was close to Vera's house, or they wouldn't have dashed to find Jess in such a panic. Jess could only suppose they'd heard a report from an observation post.

An ARP Warden stopped the car before they could turn into Farthing Lane. 'You can't go any further. Road's closed. Bloody bomb's blasted a massive 'ole right in the middle of the street.'

'Was anyone...' Jess hesitated, unable to bring herself to say 'killed' in the superstitious fear that saying it would make it true. 'Anyone 'urt?' she said finally.

'Three 'ouses flattened. We ain't found no bodies, but...' the warden concluded with an expressive gesture that conveyed the futility of any search. 'Anyway, we can't get near 'em yet. It's like the infernos of 'ell up there.'

'Which 'ouses? What numbers?'

'No idea. Sorry, love.'

Milan parked the car. The instant she heard the click of the handbrake, Jess fumbled to find the door handle and scrambled out. She clutched Milan's arm. 'We 'ave to look for them. They're still alive, I know it.' Surely she would have felt if anything had happened to Hannah?

Ignoring the warden's protest, she marched up the street, having no problem matching Milan's strides now. The moment they rounded the corner, Jess stopped dead as a wall of heat struck her face. She coughed, her eyes smarting. Blinking, she strained to see through the smoke to see the damage. The centre of the inferno was four houses down the terrace from Jack and Vera's house. She could instantly see that there was no hope for anyone who had been in that house or the ones to either side. The scene was so changed that it took a while to work out which house was Jack and Vera's. When she saw it her heart went cold. It wasn't ablaze – not yet, at any rate, although the flames were licking closer. It hadn't suffered a direct hit, but the blast had reduced the top floor to rubble. She heard someone moan, a sound like an animal in pain. She broke into a run, wanting to fling herself onto the rubble and dig for Hannah and Vera but strong arms caught her and held her back. It was only then that she realised the moan she'd heard had come from her.

'Wait. You will only make things worse.' Milan spoke in her ear. He stopped and coughed but didn't loosen his grip.

'Hannah. Hannah's in there. I 'ave to get 'er out.'

'Wait.' Milan coughed again. Jess, too, needed to clear her throat against the choking dust and smoke that filled the air. When he spoke again, his voice was stronger. 'We could bring the whole lot down unless we act with care.'

Jess wanted to scream with impatience. Milan's advice made sense, however. They moved as close as they could to Vera and Jack's house before one of the firemen stopped her. 'Stand back, love. The whole place could come down at any moment.'

She took a step back and searched desperately, eyes streaming, for any sign of life inside. After a while she noticed a commotion a few feet away. A man struggled against two burly firemen who seemed to be preventing the man from hurling himself into the crumbling house. The man twisted in his attempt to break free and in doing so, turned his face briefly towards Jess, revealing the thin face, aquiline nose and bushy eyebrows of her uncle.

The sight brought back movement to her limbs. 'Uncle Jack,' she cried, racing towards him. She grasped his arm, forcing him to cease his struggles. 'Uncle Jack, you're safe.'

Jack turned wild eyes upon her. 'Gone. Everything's gone.'

'Vera and Hannah – where are they?' Jess had to restrain herself from shaking her uncle.

Jack shook his head. He pulled his hat from his head and turned it over and over in his hands. 'I was at the Dog and Duck, 'avin' a pint with Alf and Vic. Vic's youngest just 'ad a baby boy so we were celebrating, like.'

It was only the knowledge that Jack was in shock that enabled Jess to resist the urge to grab him by the collar. Milan had caught up with her by this time, and, after exchanging glances with Jess, he wrapped an arm around Jack's shoulders and steered him away from the fire.

All the resistance seemed to drain from Jack; he allowed himself to be guided to a spot well away from the blaze, where he sank down upon the kerb. 'It's a little boy,' he said to no one in particular. 'They're calling 'im Billy after 'is dad.'

'I'll look after 'im, love. A good tot of brandy'll see 'im right.'

Jess looked up to see a wiry middle-aged woman bending over them, holding an enamel mug and a small bottle of brandy – the type housewives over the land kept for 'medicinal purposes'. She wore a dressing gown, and her hair was done up in curlers and wrapped in a scarf. Even in her nightwear, nothing could take away the air of authority that clung to her. Jess had lived in fear of her as a child, always taking care not to get into her bad books and earn the sharp side of her tongue. Now, however, Jess was relieved to see her.

'Mrs Prosser, 'ave you seen Vera and… and…?' she couldn't bring herself to say Hannah's name.

'Why, it's young Jess 'alloway. I didn't recognise you there. Bad business,' Mrs Prosser said, with a nod towards the blaze. 'Came out of nowhere, it did. No warning, no nothing.'

But Jess was in no mood to make conversation. 'Mrs Prosser, I need to find Auntie Vera and Hannah. They weren't—?' She swallowed.

'They're inside.' It was Uncle Jack who spoke. 'I 'ave to find them.'

It felt as though the breath was being squeezed from Jess's lungs. She had clung to the hope that Vera and Hannah had also been out of the house. A grey mist swirled in front of her eyes; the noise of shouting and the roaring fire receded.

Then a voice cut through. Milan's voice. 'I will look for them.'

Jess drew a gulping breath, forcing herself to concentrate. 'Not alone,' she said.

She had to forget that every extra second they wasted could be the last second of air for Hannah and Vera. Resisting the urge to run up to the terrace and scrabble among the fallen bricks, she examined the house carefully, looking for signs of life. It soon became clear that shifting rubble from the front might cause more of the house to collapse. The side wall closest to the blast had fallen away, and most of the front had gone too, making the house look like a dolls house that had been opened up. The hall and stairwell were clearly visible; the roof had fallen in, covering the front bedroom and the front room downstairs. She couldn't see clearly how badly the back of the house was damaged, although it was obvious they would have to move a lot of rubble to get through.

Milan must have reached the same conclusion. 'Can we get round the back?' he asked.

The question galvanised her into action. 'Yes, there's an alley. This way.'

She grabbed his arm and led him to one of the side passages that cut through the terrace at intervals. They squeezed through the narrow gap to a path running parallel to the rear of the terrace. From here they were able to reach the gate leading to Jack and Vera's back yard. Jess pushed it open and staggered through. To her relief she saw the rear of the building was fairly intact. Great cracks scored the brickwork and lumps of masonry were missing near the roof. Through the roar of the flames farther down the street, she could hear ominous creaks and groans shuddering through the house.

She ran to the back door and pushed. It wouldn't budge. A glance showed why: the door frame had buckled, jamming the door. She shoved harder. 'Help me get it open.'

Milan added his weight and they managed to force it inwards a couple of inches before it stuck fast. 'There must be something blocking it on the other side,' Milan said. 'I'll try the windows.'

During the Blitz, Uncle Jack had boarded up the windows at the back of the house after they had been shattered during a raid. They had been fixed from the outside so there was no pushing them inwards, and they didn't have the tools to lever out the nails. Milan grabbed a brick from the rubble on the ground and bashed it in the middle of the boards, making a large dent. Seeing what he was trying to do, Jess snatched up another brick and joined in. If they could make a hole in the flimsy hardboard, they could use it as a handhold to lever the boarding off the window frames.

The exertion, together with the heat from the fire, made her shirt stick to her back as she struck the board over and over again. A glance at Milan showed his hair cling to his forehead with perspiration. She stopped to gather her breath and watched him strike one more time. The wood splintered, leaving a jagged hole.

Jess immediately lunged at the window and stood on tiptoe to look through. A wave of plaster dust hit her in the face, setting her coughing again. 'Hannah!' she shouted. 'Vera!'

The ceiling had caved in, covering everything in plaster. Hannah's bed dangled from the hole, wedged against a beam. Judging from the way the beams creaked, the house was facing imminent collapse. 'Hannah!' she shouted again.

Had that been an answering cry? Jess froze, listening. It was no good, though. There was far too much noise from the firefighters and the roaring flames, the collapsing rubble. Grasping the jagged edges of boarding around the hole she gave it a violent tug. The board jerked free from two of the nails.

'Here. Let me do it.' Milan stood beside her. 'You will cut your hands doing it like that.' He stripped off his tunic and wrapped it around his right hand before reaching into the hole and yanking the board, his face screwed up with the effort. It tore free from the window frame with a grinding, splintering noise.

The moment the window was clear, Jess moved to throw herself across the sill. Milan, however, held her back. 'No. One of us must stay outside in case we need help.'

'I'll go in. I'm smaller. I can fit through narrow gaps.'

'*I* will go. I am stronger. I might need to lift them clear.'

As panicked as Jess was, she could see the sense in Milan's words. She moved aside to let him enter, shining her torch inside to give him enough light to see by. There was no need to worry about blackout regulations: the fire gave enough light to pinpoint the street for any bombers. With her heart beating painfully, she watched him haul himself over the ledge and drop inside. The exposed beams in the ceiling gave another creak.

'Hurry. It's going to come down any minute.' A sudden roar made her shoot a glance over her shoulder. 'Oh, God, next door's roof's on fire.' For a few seconds she stared, mesmerised, at the fountain of flame in the night sky. A moment later, she leaned across the sill, heedless of the splinters digging into her arms. 'Hannah!' she screamed.

She broke off, coughing, her throat raw and looked at Milan who was searching under the collapsed ceiling with agonising thoroughness. 'Anything?'

Milan shook his head, shining his own torch into the corners.

Then she heard a cry. Looking up she saw a small face peering down from above through the gaping hole. She shone her torch light up, revealing Hannah, clinging to one of the bed's legs.

'Hannah!' Jess felt limp with relief, although Hannah wasn't safe yet.

Hannah looked at Jess and edged closer to the hole. 'Jess.' Tears streaked Hannah's grimy face.

'Don't move. We'll get you down.'

Milan picked his way across the rubble to stand beneath Hannah. He reached up. His hands didn't quite reach as high as Hannah. 'Hold onto the bed and lower yourself down,' he told her. 'I will catch you.'

Hannah nodded and eased herself towards the hole and Milan's waiting arms.

'What about Auntie Vera?' Jess called. 'Is she up there too?'

Hannah shook her head, her face crumpling. 'She went downstairs just before… before…' She broke off with a sob.

'Don't worry, sweetheart. We'll find her. Let's get you to safety first.' Jess could see Hannah was trembling so hard she was scared the girl would freeze before she could lower herself through the hole. She held her breath. She had never felt so helpless, knowing her daughter and aunt were in danger and there was nothing she could do to help them.

Chapter Sixteen

Inch by inch, Hannah wriggled closer to the edge of the hole, her right arm wrapped around the leg of the bed. Now her left foot dangled over the void. She wore pyjamas made from brushed cotton with a pattern of seashells. Hannah was growing out of them – the legs only reached to mid-calf and rode up to Hannah's knees as she wormed her way over the edge. Her bare feet were smeared with grey dust and streaks of blood from several scratches. Funny how you noticed little things like that.

Hannah's sobs turned to a keening wail as her left foot flailed in the air.

'That's it, Hannah. Nearly there. You're doing so well.' Jess strove to keep the panic from her voice, tried to ignore the growing heat on the side of her face that told her the fire blazed only yards away.

Milan, stretching to his full height managed to grasp both Hannah's legs below the knee. 'There you go. I have got you. Let go of the bed now. I will not let you fall.'

The last words had hardly left his mouth when the upper floor gave a lurch. Hannah squealed and gripped the bed even harder. Roof tiles fell from above, through the bedroom to smash with a clatter on the ground. Even when one struck Milan's elbow, he didn't release his grip from Hannah's legs. Some fell outside. Jess heard the brittle slates shatter upon the paving slabs. She thrust her head through the window to avoid getting hit.

Jess's throat closed in terror. She tried to call out to Hannah, to reassure her. No words would come. All she could do was grip the window sill, feeling cold brick scrape beneath her fingernails, as she watched the two most precious people in her life face peril.

Then Milan spoke. His voice was so calm, Jess felt her heart rate ease. 'I am still here, Hannah. Take your time.'

It was probably a good thing Jess couldn't get any words out, for she knew she wouldn't be able to utter anything so calming. She would probably have screamed something that would have thrown Hannah into an even greater panic. Milan, on the other hand, continued to speak words of encouragement as though he were doing nothing more risky than soothing a frightened animal. Finally, Hannah drew a shuddering breath and released her hold on the bed. She slid through the hole to be caught securely in Milan's arms. An instant later, he handed her through the window, and Jess hugged her daughter close, tears dripping into Hannah's matted hair.

Milan's voice broke through her sobs. 'Take her to the first aiders on the street. I will get your aunt.'

By the time Jess had managed to prise Hannah out of her arms so the first aiders could take a look at her, she was torn. Half of her couldn't bear to leave Hannah for a moment, wanted to cling to her, reassure herself she was safe. Then one of the firefighters clutched her arm. 'Did you say there was still someone in the house?'

She nodded. 'My aunt. My friend is looking for her.'

'Get them out now. We can't hold the fire back much longer.'

After giving Hannah one last hug and seeing her safely reunited with Uncle Jack, she rushed back to the yard. 'Milan,' she shouted the moment she was through the gate. 'Where are you?'

She reached the window just as a rumble and a crash sounded within. 'Milan!' She peered inside, shining her torch through the window but could see nothing through a billowing cloud of dust. It caught at her throat, making her choke, and stung her eyes. The fire scorched the side of her face but a gnawing chill froze her insides. What if Milan and Vera were trapped within, listening to the house fall around them and the fire approaching but unable to move? 'Milan!' She tried to shout his name. It came out as a croak.

Then came the rending sound of shifting wood. An odd, hunched figure emerged through the dust. Jess blinked, trying to force the image into focus through a mist of shimmering tears. Then the sight resolved itself into Milan, supporting Vera, shuffling towards the window. Sobbing, she reached forward to help Vera. She hardly knew how they managed to drag her through. Then she was hugging her aunt hard.

'Thank God,' she gasped. 'Are you hurt?'

She would have checked Vera over, but Milan tugged her arm. 'We must get away before the fire reaches us.'

Jess nodded and put her arm around Vera to help her through to the street.

–

'Thank you. For everything.' Jess, feeling limp from delayed reaction, clung to Milan's arm as they walked back to the car. 'If it weren't for you...' she shuddered and pressed closer to Milan's side.

It was several hours later, Jess not wanting to leave her family until she was sure they were well and had shelter. Vera, while being bruised and dazed, had miraculously escaped serious injury. Mrs Prosser had kindly allowed Vera, Jack and Hannah to use her spare room for as long as they needed. Once Jess had bathed the dust from Hannah and treated her numerous scratches, she had put her to bed, dressed in a borrowed nightie. The little girl had clung to her, crying, and it had taken over an hour for her to calm down enough to sleep, clutching a toy rabbit another of their neighbours had given her. Before leaving, she had also given Vera and Jack all the money she had in her possession, little though it was. She had been moved but not surprised by how the whole street had come out in support, rallying round with clothes, food and shelter for those who had lost their homes.

'You do not have to thank me. I would never have let you face that alone,' Milan replied.

Jess gazed into Milan's face. 'I know. And it means so much to me.'

She had first been drawn to Milan because of his good looks and the glamour that clung to him as a pilot. As their friendship progressed, she couldn't understand what it was about him that made it so difficult to stick to her intention of having fun but not getting too close. Now it hit her that the strength of his affection had made it impossible for her to forget him. Not his feelings but the way he made it clear he would always be there for her if she needed him. While she had flirted with other men, her relationship with Milan had never felt like simple flirtation, no matter how many times she had denied any deeper feelings.

'Why did you wait so long for me?' she asked.

He frowned. 'I couldn't leave you. The underground will have stopped running by now.'

She bit back a laugh. 'Not tonight. I mean, after I left Amberton.'

His face cleared. 'Oh. That is easy. No other woman has the combination of fire and compassion and fun. You are the only one for me. I have always known that.'

Another time she could have resisted the surge of feeling for him. There was something so poignant about his simple declaration, said in such a matter-of-fact tone, said, she was sure, with no expectation of return. Combined with her relief and gratitude, there was no resisting the impulse. She couldn't hold back any longer. Standing on tiptoe, she leant forward and pulled the peaked cap from his head. Then, bracing her hands on his arms, she pressed her lips to his.

For a moment, Milan stood motionless. That awful split-second when she thought he would reject her advance told Jess all she needed to know about her feelings for him. Then he wrapped his arms around her, pulling her close, deepening the kiss. It was a good thing he held her so tight, or she was sure her legs wouldn't support her. She pressed so close she could feel the hammering of his heart. Or was it hers? She was no longer sure. She slid her hands up his arms then wound her arms around his neck. After holding back for so long, now she never wanted to let him go. All she was aware of was the feel of his lips upon hers, the warmth of his body in contrast to the chill night air and the roar of blood in her ears.

'Steady on, you two. Ain't you got somewhere else to go?'

Jess stepped back in time to see the dark shape of an ARP Warden walk past. For once she was grateful for the blackout, as it hid her face which burned red hot.

Milan took her arm. 'Come. Let us find the car.'

They walked a few steps towards the road where they had parked. Then Milan said, 'Just to be clear, I kissed you back because I want us to be together. If you do not feel the same, I trust you to say so.'

'I—' several conflicting thoughts came to mind, tying her tongue. She knew beyond any doubt that she wanted to be with him, but she also knew she wasn't good enough for him. Well, wasn't it time he knew that? She couldn't break with him, not again. However, if he knew the truth, he would do it for her.

She gulped. 'I do feel the same but there's something you need to know.'

'Jess, if it's about the other men you saw after leaving Amberton, I do not mind.'

'No. It's something else. It's important.'

Milan stopped, pulling them into a shop doorway so they couldn't be overheard by any passers-by. 'Then tell me.'

Jess drew a deep breath. It was all very well deciding to tell him the truth, but this was something she had hidden for years. Not even Evie and May knew. 'It's hard for me to say. I don't know how to begin.'

'Begin at the beginning. That is what my *babi* – my grandmother – used to say.'

Jess nodded. She found she was shaking, her stomach churning. Why was she doing this? If she kept quiet, Milan need never know. Never know the worst of her. Although telling him was the best way to put him at a distance, she dreaded seeing the change in the way he looked at her. The sudden coldness in his expression. How long before he would suddenly come up with an excuse to explain why he couldn't see her any more?

She removed her hand from his arm, not wanting to experience the rejection of him throwing off her hold. Balling her fists at her sides to conceal the trembling in her hands, she began. But where was the beginning of this particular sorry tale?

'You know I was an actress before the war,' she said finally. When Milan nodded, she went on, 'It was a tough profession to get into. Maybe I had my head turned by doing well in local plays when I was still at school, but I soon learned my mistake. I'd go for endless auditions, and the waiting room would be full of other girls, all better looking and more talented.'

'I cannot believe that.'

Despite the cold nausea gnawing at her stomach, Jess managed to flash Milan a grateful smile. 'Flatterer,' she said. 'But believe it. London was teeming with girls all wanting to make it big on stage or screen. There wasn't much hope for a working-class girl like me with no connections.'

'You did get work, though.'

Jess nodded, swallowing. Now she was getting to the point of her story and she was finding it harder to force out the words. 'I got lucky.' She gave a harsh laugh. 'Or I thought I was lucky.' The eventual consequences had been far from lucky. 'My favourite teacher, Miss Barrows, married a playwright.' Jess remembered Miss Barrows with affection. Miss Barrows had always encouraged her, telling Jess she had talent, feeding her dreams. 'When he got one of his plays into a small theatre off the West End, she put in a good word for me. He got me a small speaking part. Once I got my foot in the door, I managed to get other roles. All small parts, but they gave me hope I'd get my big break.' It was funny, she reflected, how she had never been satisfied. When she'd started out, she'd looked in awe at the young women who had managed to get small speaking parts, thinking she'd be happy if only she could do the same. Then, when she'd got her first role, she'd been envious of the actresses regularly getting major roles. She supposed that if she'd ever achieved top billing in a play, she'd have been envious of Hollywood actresses. She never felt that way in the WAAF, even though there was a rigid hierarchy. Maybe it was because everyone worked as a team, supporting each other, knowing how vital it was for each person to succeed.

'Did you get your big break?'

'Nearly.' Her voice caught. 'That's when I met Leo – Leonard Steele. I'd got a part as a chambermaid in a murder mystery play, and he was playing the lead – the detective.'

The sky was turning a pale grey, heralding sunrise. Looking over Milan's shoulder, she could see shopkeepers unlocking doors and opening awnings. A newspaper boy was setting up on a street corner. Jess hugged her arms to her chest, shivering in the cold air. A new day was dawning, and she should return to Bentley Manor to snatch some sleep before going on duty later that afternoon. Now she had started, though, she wanted – needed – to finish.

'Leo took an interest in me. Said I had talent. Said he could help me make it big if… if…'

She saw from the sudden widening of Milan's eyes the moment when comprehension dawned. She hastily looked away, not wanting to see his expression harden. The disgust.

She rushed on. 'I really thought I loved 'im. Leo was so charming, flattering me, telling me I was the only girl for 'im.' She swallowed. 'If I didn't love 'im, I'd 'ave never…' She wasn't usually stuck for words, but she couldn't bring herself to say what had happened next.

'He made you promises. Said you were the only girl for him.'

Jess looked at Milan in surprise. While his expression was grim, there didn't seem to be any disgust aimed at her. 'Yes.'

'And you thought you were the only one he spoke to like that.'

'Yes,' she said again. It was the only word she could manage. Any minute now he would turn his back, walk away. No, she corrected herself, he wouldn't leave her here alone. He would see her safely back to Stanmore before coming up with a sudden reason why he wouldn't be able to see her again.

Milan raked his fingers through his hair, leaving a fresh smear of grime across his forehead. 'You are not the first girl to fall for a man's lies.'

Lies? Suddenly she was looking at her early relationship with Leo through the eyes of experience rather than remembering it as it had happened when she had been so young and naive. 'I… why didn't I see it before? I was young. Only seventeen. He seduced me.'

Milan's expression was grim. Any minute now he would make an excuse why he couldn't see her any more. Oh, he'd be kind; he wouldn't say it was because he couldn't bear to be with another man's leavings, but she would know.

Suddenly she was gabbling, almost pleading. 'I 'ad no idea. I mean, my auntie 'ad warned me not to let my 'ead get turned, but I 'adn't really understood…' If someone had asked why she was trying to justify her mistakes when she had started her confession with the intention of driving him away, she couldn't have said.

'Jess.' Milan's voice was gentle. She dared to meet his gaze and found no condemnation. Nothing but sympathy. 'You do not need to explain yourself to me.'

She shook her head as though it would help her make sense of her confusion. 'I don't understand.' Where was the disgust, the angry declaration that he could have nothing to do with a girl like her?

'You made a mistake in believing the lies of a *vûl* like Leonard Steele. I do not believe that means you should suffer for that mistake for the rest of your life. In my eyes, Leonard Steele was far more in the wrong than you. Do you see him suffer for it, or being eaten up by guilt?'

'He wouldn't, would 'e? He's a man. Men can get away with murder, whereas women just have to wear their hemlines a fraction too high or their neckline a tad too low, and they're labelled hussies to the end of their days. That's the way the world has always been.'

'That does not make it right.'

Jess searched Milan's face, looking for any sign of revulsion. She found nothing but compassion.

The newspaper boy shouted out the daily headlines, making her jump, and there was a rattle as a greengrocer opened up the shutters of her shop. Milan made a move as though to turn away and resume their walk.

'Wait.' Jess grabbed his arm. She couldn't let him leave without knowing the worst. She closed her fingers upon his sleeve, bunching the cloth and twisting it in her fist. 'Hannah ain't my cousin,' she said in a rush. 'She's my daughter.'

Chapter Seventeen

Milan's heart melted at the sight of Jess's face, her eyes wide and fearful. He had never known her be anything other than courageous and unflinching, so for her to shrink from him spoke volumes about the burden her secret must have been.

He couldn't bear to see her this way, hands clenched into fists at her side as though she were bracing herself for rejection. He pulled her into his arms; with a sound that sounded partway between a sigh and a sob, she rested her head in the crook of his neck. 'Oh, Jess.' He kissed the top of her head. 'I understand now.' It explained so much about her, why she had always tried to push him away whenever he got too close to her secrets.

She pulled back, although only enough so she could frown up at him. 'I don't understand,' she said. 'I thought you wouldn't want anything to do with me.'

If he could lay his hands on Leonard Steele right now, he would make a mess of that handsome, cocky face. 'If I were to reject everyone who has ever made a mistake, I would be very lonely.' He caught both her hands in his own, warming the chilled skin, doing everything he could to reassure her with his actions as well as his words. 'However, if I condemn you, I must also condemn my sister.'

'Your sister?' The frown line between Jess's eyes deepened. 'Then your nephew—?'

'Is better off not knowing the conniving, smooth-talking bastard who is his father. He left my sister broken-hearted when she told him he had left her with child.' He made no attempt to hide the rage that bubbled up when he thought of the speed with which the man had left his sister's life after she had told him she was pregnant with his child.

'Leo didn't leave me. I left him.' Jess held his gaze as though willing him to think worse of her. 'I never told him I was pregnant.'

Milan wasn't going to let Leo escape condemnation so easily. 'Did he ever ask? It should have occurred to him it was possible.'

Jess shook her head and studied her shoes. He could see she had taken all the shame onto herself, was blaming herself and excusing Leo.

'Jess,' he said gently, 'We all make mistakes. I do not believe it is right that women should be made to feel more shame than men.'

'Then you don't—?'

Milan answered her the best way he knew how. He tilted her face to his with a finger under her chin and kissed her, pouring all the love and comfort he wanted her to feel into the kiss. Above all, he felt light-headed with relief. He hadn't known Jess long before her courage and loyalty, combined with her fun-loving nature, had made her stand out in his mind above all the other girls he had known. She hadn't struck him as cruel, so had found it hard to understand why she had refused all contact with him after she left Amberton, declaring she had never loved him. Now it was clear she had just been trying to protect herself from the hurt of what she had foreseen as the inevitable rejection when he learned the truth.

When the need to breathe forced him to break the kiss, Jess laid her head upon his shoulder with a small sigh. 'I'm sorry I doubted you,' she said. 'I thought you wouldn't want anything to do with me once you found out.'

'You could have kept it secret,' he said, stroking her hair. 'Why did you not?'

Jess lifted her head and leaned back to look into his face, her blue eyes serious. 'I could never let you go on believing a lie. Not when I'm...' Something in her expression changed and suddenly she was the forthright, brave young woman he knew her to be. 'Not when I'm falling in love with you.'

It was something he had known ever since their first dance before the Battle of Britain; he would never have pursued her so single-mindedly if he hadn't believed his feelings to be returned. To hear her admit her feelings, however, made him giddy with joy. Finally Jess was letting him see the woman beneath the flashy, flirty veneer. 'I am in love with you, too, but I think you already knew that.'

Jess's answering smile made his heart skip. 'Ah, but I don't know what made you fall for me in the first place.'

He didn't even need to pause to think. 'It was the first time we all went to the pub together, after our first lesson.' By 'we', he meant the Czechoslovakian members of Brimstone squadron, whom Jess and Evie had been ordered to teach English. Newly arrived in England, burning with hatred for the Nazis who had overrun his country, he had been impatient with Fighter Command for denying him the right to fly combat missions and had taken out his impatience on Evie during their first lesson. Evie's cool handling of the situation had impressed him, but it was Jess, and her loyal defence of her friend at the pub later, who had captured his heart. 'Even then I saw there was more to you than met the eye. It makes me happy that you trust me enough to show me who you are at heart.'

Her smile growing brighter, Jess said, 'You mean you can finally see the tree beneath the tangle of ivy?'

He laughed. 'It is very beautiful ivy, but it cannot match the tree at the core.'

A playful light danced in Jess's eyes. 'Tell me, what kind of tree am I? If you say oak, I may need to stop eating all the potatoes we're given in the mess.'

'Not an oak. An oak is...' he groped for the right word and could only adequately describe them using a musical term. 'Is *largo*. Wide and slow. Dignified.'

Jess's nose wrinkled. 'I don't think any girl would appreciate being described that way.'

'I shall remember that.'

'So go on – what am I?'

He paused for a moment while he thought. 'You are a birch. Light and silvery. Shimmering. *Allegro*.'

'Now you're talking.'

'Ah, but there are more to birches than meet the eye. They survive storms that can fell great oaks, and they thrive in conditions too harsh for other trees. They are beautiful but also strong. Very strong.'

Jess laid her head back on his shoulder, blinking. After a moment she ran her thumb under her eyes; her hand trembled slightly. 'Do you really not mind about Hannah?' she asked eventually. 'I thought you would run a mile.'

'I knew you were hiding something,' he answered. 'Something that meant we could have no future. I feared maybe you were married. But this...' He paused, wishing he did not have to express himself in a language not his own. He wanted to be sure there was no misunderstanding. 'It is important, yes. A big part of you. But it does not stop us being together.'

'It would stop many men. That's why I've never told anyone before. Are all Czech men as understanding as you?'

'Czech men are no different from British men. Maybe what happened to my sister made me see more clearly.'

It was only much later, after he had seen Jess back to Stanmore and he was on his way to rejoin his squadron that the significance of something he had said hit him. He had said he had feared Jess had been hiding something that meant they had no future together. But now he had real hope the Allies would soon free Czechoslovakia from the Nazis, did that not mean he would return home? What future was there for him and Jess if her life lay in Britain and his in Czechoslovakia?

–

'Are your aunt and Hannah going to be okay?' May handed Jess a cup of cocoa then perched on the edge of Jess's bed. She and Evie had just returned from their evening watch and Jess, refreshed from an afternoon spent asleep, felt more able to talk than she had when she had seen her friends that morning.

When Jess had finally stumbled into Bentley Manor while the off-duty officers were still having breakfast, the Medical Officer had taken one look at her grimy, tear-streaked face and hustled her into a bath, telling her in no uncertain terms that she was suffering from shock and was not going on duty that day. While Jess had sat in the bath, scrubbing the layers of dust and soot from her skin and hair, she had been surprised by a sudden shaking fit. When she'd emerged from the bathroom, the MO had ordered her straight to bed and dosed her with a cup of strong tea, liberally laced with brandy.

'They're going to be fine. Which is more than can be said for my uniform.' Jess eyed the torn, grimy tunic and skirt hanging from the back of the door. She feared no amount of cleaning would get rid of the strong smell of smoke.

'We'll deal with it. Don't worry.' Evie perched on the foot of the bed. 'But don't think you can pull the wool over our eyes. We both saw the state you were in this morning. Don't try and pretend you're only worried about your clothes.'

Jess blew the steam from her cocoa, breathing in the rich smell of chocolate. It seemed Milan wasn't the only one to refuse to let her get away with brushing off her worries with a laugh. 'I don't mind admitting I was terrified,' she said finally. 'When I saw that crater...' She shuddered. 'But I mustn't dwell on what never happened. They're safe. That's all that matters.'

'Where will they live?' May asked.

'Vera's taking Hannah back to Wales until Uncle Jack can sort out a house. I'm going to see them onto the train tomorrow. With so many people in the East End being made homeless, who knows how long that will take.' Jess took another breath of the cocoa. 'Funny. I was so anxious to get Vera to go back to Welshpool, I'm really going to miss them once they go. Now I've actually seen the results of the V2s, I can see things from Vera's point of view. I understand now why she was so reluctant to let the Nazis make her leave her own home. In a strange way, it feels like we're letting them win.'

Somehow it was hard to feel too angry about anything. Of course, it would have been different had the worst happened and Vera and Hannah been killed or wounded. But with her mind at ease over her family, Jess couldn't help her thoughts drifting to Milan and that glorious kiss. Thinking about it now, she smiled as she sipped her cocoa.

Wait. Cocoa? She frowned at May and Evie. 'Where did the cocoa come from?'

Evie grinned. 'Laura Morgan got it. You know she's dating that American pilot? He's been able to get hold of all sorts of things for her. Talking of which.' Evie pulled something from her pocket.

Jess stared at it. 'No way. That's never an orange.'

'Believe it.'

'You're 'avin' me on. That's a round lump of clay someone's painted orange.'

'Here.' Evie threw it to Jess who caught it. 'It's all yours. Laura decided your need was greater than hers.'

Jess held the orange cupped in her hands. 'I can't remember the last time I 'ad one of these.' She held it to her face, caressing the glossy, dimpled skin and breathed in the tangy sweet scent. She moaned with delight. 'Tell me I'm not dreaming.'

'You're not dreaming.'

Just the smell set her mouth watering. Her yearning to peel it and pop a juicy orange segment in her mouth was so strong she could almost taste the burst of citrusy flavour on her tongue. She gave a regretful glance at Evie and May. 'You know I would share this with you, don't you?'

They nodded.

'But… oh, I can't believe I'm doing this, but you don't mind if I give it to Hannah, do you? Poor girl doesn't remember stuff like oranges and bananas. If she's got to go back to Welshpool to those 'orrible kids, the least I can do is give 'er the orange.'

'Course we don't mind,' May said.

'Can I have one last sniff before you put it away?' Evie asked.

'Me too.' May raised her hand like an eager pupil in school.

Grinning, Jess tossed the orange to May and watched as her friends took turns to breathe in the orange's scent. 'Maybe one of us should get an American boyfriend.'

Evie gave Jess a significant look, her brows arched. 'Funny. I thought you were more than happy with Milan.'

Despite herself, Jess couldn't control the soppy grin she knew was spreading across her face.

'Hah!' Evie pointed a triumphant finger at Jess. 'I knew it. Come on, own up. Tell us what happened.'

Jess settled back against her pillows. 'He was wonderful.' Realising she hadn't yet told her friends anything besides assuring them her family was safe, she described in detail what Milan had done to rescue Hannah and Vera. 'And then… well, I couldn't resist. I just kissed him in full view of the whole street.'

'Out of gratitude or because you love him?' Evie fixed her with a penetrating stare. Sometimes Jess wished Evie didn't speak her mind quite so freely.

'Love. Definitely love.' Jess hadn't been so sure about anything in her life. 'I've been in love with him for ages. I just…' She paused. Telling Milan the truth about Hannah had been liberating. His understanding had taken a weight off her shoulders. Yet she couldn't bring herself to tell Evie and May. Not yet. She was nearly certain they wouldn't reject her. Even so, they would never regard her in the same way once they knew the truth. Jess didn't think she could bear any change in their friendship at the moment. However, that did make it more difficult to explain why she had held back from a commitment to Milan until now. 'I wasn't convinced he really loved me. When I saw him fling himself into a crumbling house for the sake of my family, I knew then that he must love me after all.'

Thankfully, neither of her friends seemed to have noticed her hesitation. May gave a great sigh and gazed dreamily at the ceiling. 'Isn't it wonderful we all have boyfriends now? I was worried you would feel left out before, but now you've got Milan.'

'Yes. I've got Milan. And we've got each other, too.' It must be the events of the previous night catching up with her, because she had to blink back tears. May and Evie seemed similarly affected. While they might have had boyfriends for most of the time they had been friends, Jess knew their friendship was just as important to them as it was to her. Neither Evie nor May had had any friends before joining the WAAF. Although Jess had friends at school, she had let them drift away during her single-minded pursuit of acting success. Jess knew she would never let another man or her career, however important either were to her, come between her and her friends.

'What about Leonard Steele?' Evie asked. Jess knew a twinge of discomfort as Evie went on, 'Does *he* know you are with Milan?'

'Leo and I are just friends. And he knows about Milan.' Jess paused. 'Well, he knows I've been seeing him.' She couldn't possibly have told Leo how she felt about Milan when she had scarcely admitted it even to herself.

May placed the orange onto Jess's bedside cabinet with a look of regret then said, 'Does he know you're not interested in being more than friends?' Knowing her, despite what Jess had told her friends about Leo mixing with a wild crowd, she probably worried that Leo was secretly in love.

'Don't worry. I've made it quite clear. He knows nothing's going to happen between us.'

Evie leaned forward and propped her elbows on her knees. The bedsprings creaked as she moved. 'Why does he still want to take you out then?'

'Oh, thanks! So it can't be for the pleasure of my company?'

Evie had the grace to look embarrassed. 'Sorry. I didn't mean it like that. But doesn't it strike you as odd? Why single out a woman who's already rejected him when there are no end of rich and famous women who would love to be seen with him?'

That gave Jess pause for thought. She had been so occupied in justifying her friendship with Leo, persuading herself it was good for her career, that she hadn't considered what Leo stood to gain. Then she dismissed it with a wave of the hand. 'Probably just the novelty of a new face. I'm sure he'll drop me once the film is finished.'

'So you'll carry on seeing him for now?'

'I'll have to. I'll still be needed for film business.' Seeing how unhappy Evie looked, Jess added, 'Look, I admit I was flattered by his attention at first and maybe got swept away by the glamour of filming.'

'Maybe?' Evie arched her brows.

'Okay, definitely. But I'm over it now.' She couldn't deny filming had been fun and a welcome break from routine. Nevertheless, it would be good to be back in the

Filter Room. Back in the centre of the action, where she knew her work was important.

'Glad to hear it.' Evie gave her an approving nod. She picked up a copy of the *Times* that she had brought for Jess. 'Now, who wants to help me do the crossword?'

Jess only put half her mind to unravelling the clues. The rest of her thoughts were occupied in reliving Milan's kisses. Could she finally leave her past behind and dare to think he could be part of her future?

Chapter Eighteen

Autumn merged into Winter. The days grew shorter and darker, and when the girls went for walks on the common, their path was strewn with thick piles of crisp bronze leaves, rimed with frost. The film company recalled Jess a couple of times to film some extra scenes and do voice recordings, all fitted, as they had agreed, around her regular duties. When the last of the extra sessions were over, she had expected to hear no more from Leo. To her surprise, however, he had invited her several times to join the rest of the film crew in the same night club as before.

Evie and May had disapproved, she could tell, although they said nothing. Jess had just sensed their silent reproof each time she did her hair and makeup prior to Leo collecting her. If they had asked, she would have pointed out it was hardly a date as they would be mixing with the entire crew – it wasn't as if they were going for an intimate dinner for two. As they didn't ask, Jess held her tongue.

Sometimes, when she lay awake at night, she could almost hear Evie's voice asking: what does Milan think? The truth was, Milan didn't know she was meeting Leo so regularly. If she told him he would want to know why, and Jess couldn't explain to herself why she couldn't cut off all ties with Leo. He certainly wouldn't like to know that she enjoyed the stir that seemed to follow her when she was on Leo's arm.

'What are you doing for Christmas?' she asked Milan one afternoon in early December. They were walking arm in arm around Brewer's Ponds on Stanmore Common. Their breath misted and mingled in the cold air, and Jess was enjoying the excuse to snuggle close to Milan.

'I expect it will be a day like any other,' Milan said with a shrug.

'I suppose you're right.' The Allies were not advancing as fast as they had hoped. After D-Day, everyone had hoped the war in Europe would soon be over, yet the Allies still hadn't managed to retake much of Belgium and France. The V2 rockets still fell on London and eastern England and would continue to do so until the Germans had been pushed out of range.

'You sound disappointed. Were you hoping for time off?'

'No. I suppose not. I doubt I would get it after having all that time off for the film.' She tried to keep the disgruntlement from her voice. It was unfair to expect Milan to pull off some kind of magical gesture for Christmas, especially when he was flying endless missions to support the advance.

Milan pulled her closer. 'We will have our victory sooner or later. There will be time to celebrate then.'

Jess leaned her head on his shoulder with a small smile. It seemed Milan understood her better than she had thought.

There were times, though, when she wished she understood herself. After she and Milan parted at the entrance to Bentley Manor – Milan needing to return to his squadron – she was about to find a seat in the anteroom to write a letter to Hannah when Laura Morgan stuck her head around the door. 'Telephone for you, Halloway.'

Jess hurried out into the hall, her spirits reviving. It couldn't be Milan and the only other person who ever phoned was Leo. That must mean he had plans that would make up for Milan not committing to spending Christmas with her.

'What are you doing on the Saturday before Christmas?' Leo asked with little preamble after Jess had taken the call. 'Tell me you've got the evening off.'

There was no need to look up her duty schedule. She had already done so before meeting Milan. 'I have. I come off at four.'

'Excellent. The film company are throwing a Christmas party for the cast and crew. I'll pick you up at seven.'

Before she could respond, he was gone and Jess was left listening to the dial tone. She hung up the receiver and turned to see Evie and May coming downstairs.

'Who was that?' Evie asked. 'I thought you were seeing Milan today.'

'I was. That was Leo.'

'What did he want?' Evie radiated disapproval.

Jess accompanied her friends into the anteroom and flung herself into an armchair beside the fire, affecting nonchalance. 'Oh, he was just letting me know about a Christmas party the film company are throwing.'

'Are you going?' Evie sat on a sofa opposite. Instead of curling up as she usually did, she leaned forward and fixed an unwavering gaze upon Jess. May took a seat beside her, making Jess feel as though she were being interviewed.

'Course I am. You don't expect a girl to pass up an opportunity like that.'

'What about Milan?'

'He's not invited.' At that, she felt a stab of conscience. She hadn't even tried to get Milan an invite. Now she came to think of it, surely she could have invited a partner to the party as a cast member herself, rather than going as Leo's partner? It struck her that she had allowed Leo to browbeat her. She pushed the thought aside with a wave of her hand. 'Anyway, I asked what he was doing for Christmas and he said he would be busy. And he wouldn't enjoy the party.' He hadn't exactly said he would be busy. And she had asked about Christmas, not the Saturday before, which was two days before Christmas. Again, Jess pushed aside the nagging voice of her conscience.

Evie frowned. 'What are you doing, Jess? Any idiot can see you love Milan, and he's crazy about you. Please don't throw it all away.'

There was no condemnation in Evie's tone or expression, just concern. If anything, that made Jess feel worse. 'You're sounding terribly Victorian all of a sudden, Evie. I'd have thought you of all people wouldn't expect me to sit around at home if my boyfriend's not able to take me out.' Carried away on a wave of righteous indignation, she held up a finger and started to count off her justifications for going. 'First of all, it's not a date with Leo, it's a party for the whole cast and crew. Second, as I'm a member of the cast, it would be rude not to go. It would be like not joining in with celebrations in the mess. And third—' Jess groped for another reason. She was starting to wish she hadn't counted them, because if you were going to do that, you needed at least three reasons. Two was just feeble. 'And third, what I do with my free time is nobody's business but my own.' She could only hope she sounded more convincing than she felt.

Evie didn't look persuaded. She continued to look at Jess, eyebrows raised.

'Oh yeah.' Another thought struck Jess. 'I need to consider the future. Maybe I'll hear about more acting work at the party.'

Evie tilted her head. 'Have you definitely decided to go back to acting?'

'Well, it's the only job I know.' Yet again she envied Evie and May for having their futures mapped out.

Evie's expression softened. 'You'll succeed at anything you turn your mind to.' She sat back and curled up into a more comfortable position. 'Anyway, as you say, it's none of my business how you spend your free time. I don't want to see you hurt, that's all.'

'It *is* your business.' Jess felt a heel. 'We're friends. Sorry for biting your head off. It means the world to me that you and May care enough to worry.'

She hesitated. She always seemed to be on the defensive with her friends these days, probably because the truth about Hannah weighed on her mind now Leo was back on the scene. Evie and May had proved several times over that they wouldn't be judgemental, so why did she still hold back? She wiped suddenly damp palms on her skirt. Should she tell them? It would be a relief to have it in the open at last.

'I...' Her throat closed. It was no good. How did you fling a bombshell like that into a conversation? *You know my niece, Hannah? Well actually she's my daughter. Surprise! And you'll never guess who her father is.*

No, she couldn't do it. Not yet. Evie and May were waiting for her to speak, though. After floundering for a moment, she remembered she had been talking about her future career. While she felt unable to tell them the truth about Hannah, she could at least be open about her feelings on this subject. 'To be honest, I don't know if I want to be an actress again or not.'

'You must have some idea what you enjoy doing,' May said.

'I like what I'm doing now.' Her head still full of her unspoken secret, she had blurted it out without thinking. It was, she had to admit, the truth. Her WAAF work gave her a sense of achievement she didn't get from acting. She thrived on the responsibility. 'I wish I could think of a peace-time job I would enjoy as much.'

From Evie and May's expressions, she could tell they couldn't think of a suitable job either.

Jess sighed. 'So that leads me back to acting. I enjoy it, even if not as much as being a filterer. And in the meantime, I'd be an idiot not to take advantage of the contacts I've made through the film.'

Evie's lips twitched. 'In other words, you have to go to the party.'

'What can I say? It'll be a bore, but my career depends on it.'

'Then go and enjoy it.'

'I'll do my best.' She slapped her hands on her knees and rose. 'Anyway, I've got stockings to darn. Such is the life of luxury I lead.'

As soon as she was out of sight, she slumped against the wall and closed her eyes briefly. If she'd been able to confess, it would have been over and done with by now. Putting it off would only make it harder.

'You all right, Halloway?'

Jess started upright and opened her eyes to see Laura Morgan eyeing her with concern. 'Right as rain. Just tired.'

She forced a smile and ran upstairs as soon as Laura had moved away. She might have chickened out this time, but she didn't want to keep Hannah a secret from Evie and May much longer. At the next opportunity, she would tell them.

–

As Christmas approached, however, Jess couldn't seem to find the right moment. Not that she didn't have plenty of time alone with Evie and May, but there never seemed to be an appropriate opening in the conversation. Though she had to admit, she still flinched from their reaction, and didn't try too hard.

The V2s continued to rain destruction upon London, and while Jess was relieved Hannah and Vera were safe, she missed them with a persistent ache of longing. After being separated for nearly five years, she had cherished being posted near to them and found that even in a few short weeks she had grown used to them being only a ride on the Underground away. It had been wonderful to be able to visit in her free time without the need to arrange leave. Now their absence was a constant ache. She had particularly been looking forward to celebrating Hannah's sixth birthday in January; now they would yet again celebrate the day apart.

Her hours in the Filter Room were as demanding as ever. She emerged from every watch with her muscles aching. Now the nights were drawing in, she, Evie and May had less time to go for walks on the common to work out the muscles stiff from contorting themselves in odd positions to reach the tracks they were monitoring. Weeks merged into one long blur of work and sleep with precious little entertainment to brighten her days.

The only light in the darkness was Milan. He, too, was busy, seemingly having to cram the same amount of flying hours into fewer daylight hours. He only managed two further visits in the run-up to Christmas. With time so precious, Jess didn't want to waste it by provoking an argument about Leo, so kept quiet about him taking her to the party. When the party invitation had arrived from the film company, sure enough, it had been for her and a partner. She had immediately invited Milan, but he'd told her he wouldn't be able to get away. Her conscience salved that he did at least know about the party, she had held her tongue about going with Leo and let him believe she was going on her own. Which she was, really. Leo had just offered to give her a lift, that was all. She closed her mind to the voice that sounded remarkably like Evie's, asking why Leo had contacted her before the invitations had gone out, and before she had seen she would be invited in her own right.

As soon as her shift ended on the day of the party, Jess rushed back to Bentley Manor to have a bath and change into her best uniform. The skirt and tunic she had worn when going to Hannah and Vera's rescue had been mended and washed and was smart enough to wear on most occasions, but she was glad her second tunic and skirt were far smarter. By the time she had to go and meet Leo, who had parked his Bentley on Stanmore Hill, outside the WAAF officers' Mess, she was sporting bright red lipstick, her hair rolled above her collar – only lightly pinned so she could let it down the moment she was out of sight of her superior officers – and a pair of new nylon stockings that she had been delighted to find on her last shopping trip.

'Very nice,' she said, admiring the gleaming car. 'How did you manage to get petrol?'

Leo tapped his nose. 'Friends in high places. That's all I can say.'

Once she was in the car, Leo handed her a long, flat box. 'I think you'll find this more suitable than your uniform.'

Puzzled, Jess opened the lid and gasped when she lifted out a cascade of scarlet silk. 'Where did you get this?' She didn't like to ask *how* he had got it, bearing in mind clothes rationing and the scarcity of silk, which was needed for parachute production. It was a gorgeous evening dress, falling in soft folds in a vee neck over the bust, cinched to a high, tight waist, then flaring into a full skirt.

Leo looked shifty. 'Contacts in the States, you know how it is.'

Jess didn't but refrained from comment. 'I can't wear this. I have to stay in uniform.'

'No one will know.'

'They will if our photo ends up in the papers again.' At least then she had been in uniform. She dreaded to think what her CO would say if she was photographed wearing this admittedly fabulous gown. Or what Milan would think. She ran her fingers over the beading upon one of the shoulders. She could almost feel the swish of silk around her legs, so soft and light compared with her heavy uniform skirt. She hadn't worn anything as beautiful as this since the parachute silk ball gown she had worn when playing Cinderella at Amberton four years ago.

Feeling as though she were losing a part of her soul, she replaced the dress in the box and closed the lid.

Leo scowled. 'I don't think you understand how important this evening could be for you. There will be influential people there. They want to see a film star, not a dowdy WAAF.'

Jess bristled to hear herself described as dowdy. 'I'm not a film star and I am a WAAF.'

'You won't be a WAAF all your life and you could be a film star. But I guarantee no one will take you seriously if you appear in battle dress.'

Jess raised the lid then let it go, shaking her head. 'I can't wear that for a very good reason.'

'Which is?'

'It would look ridiculous with these shoes.' She pointed at the black leather lace-ups that went with her uniform. Trust a man not to consider the full outfit. She'd need more than a dress and shoes. A good outfit also required the best underwear and stockings. And what about a bag and a wrap? Jewellery? She used to spend hours considering the correct hair and makeup to set off an outfit. What was Leo expecting her to do – take off her cap and comb her hair with her fingers?

'Look in the bag on the back seat.'

It was the shoes that decided her. With some reluctance, she'd peered into the box on the back seat, half dreading that the shoes might be worth the risk. And, oh, how they were. Gold and silver peep-toe sandals with high heels and diamanté studs decorating the ankle strap. She had never in all her life imagined she would ever possess such beautiful shoes. She had to wear them.

'All right. Start driving, and keep your eyes on the road.'

She slid into the back seat. Once the car was safely away from Bentley Manor, she wriggled out of her uniform, thankful for once for the blackout, and into the dress. It felt even better than she'd imagined and fitted perfectly.

The draped neckline wasn't too revealing, meaning the underwear she'd chosen to wear didn't show. Thank goodness she'd decided to wear prettier underwear than the passion killers she usually had on under her uniform.

The shoes pinched a little, but she wasn't going to let that spoil her evening. Further investigation in the boxes contained in the bag revealed a cream cashmere stole and a tiny beaded handbag. Also a thin belt in the same scarlet as the dress; it would show off her narrow waist perfectly. No jewellery, but the matching beading on the shoulders and belt clasp was decoration enough. She arranged her skirt around her legs, enjoying the fine whisper of silk with every movement. Despite her misgivings over appearing out of uniform, she felt like a princess and decided whatever punishment she got for wearing civvies, it would be worth it.

There was no sign outside the club that a party was going on within, apart from the strains of 'Swingtime in the Rockies' that drifted into the night air whenever the door was opened. The west end street where Leo parked was so dark Jess had to strain her eyes to see the white paint marks that indicated the kerb. She took Leo's arm, purely to keep her balance in the dark on her high heels, as he led her through the doorway, down a steep flight of steps and into the club. A man in evening dress was checking invitations before letting people into the main room, although when he saw Leo he just gave him a deferential nod and waved them through. After the frosty chill outside, the heat and smoke hit Jess like a solid wall.

Any lingering resentment she held over being browbeaten into partnering Leo faded when the director approached them with an invitation to sit at his table. Jess plastered her brightest smile on her face as she took her seat and accepted a glass of champagne. She looked around the club in awe. It looked as though all the lights that had been unlit throughout the blackout had been moved into this room. A huge mirror ball swung in the centre of the dance floor, sending dazzling sparkles through the smoke haze. Everyone from the film was there, from the cameramen to the costume and makeup artists to the actors and director.

'Good to see you again, Jess,' the director said.

His wife sat next to him. She leaned forward and said, 'Everyone's been eager to meet the woman who tamed Leonard Steele's heart.' She looked Jess up and down, making her feel like a thoroughbred horse up for auction. Although Jess wasn't usually short of words, she felt a chill of horror at the woman's assertion and before she was able to utter a denial, the woman continued, 'I must say I'm surprised he's chosen a WAAF. Such a dull uniform.'

Jess couldn't let this pass. She raised her chin. 'Perhaps he sees the girl under the uniform.'

'I'm sure he does, darling,' the woman drawled. 'England is full of service women dying to show Leonard what's under their uniform. Nevertheless, I can see you possess a certain sparkle that makes you stand out. If I were you, I'd get his ring on your finger before any of these other young things get their claws into him.'

Leonard, who had been standing a little way off, talking in low tones to a man Jess recognised as his agent, now ended the conversation with a clap on the back and approached the table. Before she could assure the director's wife she had no such designs on Leo, he had swept her onto the dance floor. Jess would rather have sat for a while; her feet still throbbed and her back ached from hours of bending over the table in the Filter Room. However, she didn't protest, glad to get away from the superior woman. And, if she was honest, she enjoyed the admiring glances cast her way.

'Have you given any more thought to acting after the war?'

Jess looked at Leo in surprise. When they had danced together before he hadn't engaged in conversation, being too concerned with putting on a show for their audience. 'I've been considering it,' she said.

'Excellent,' Leo said. 'There are great opportunities for actors now the Hollywood studios are looking to extend production in England. The war has shown them how lucrative the British market can be. There has never been a better time for a British actor – or actress – to break into Hollywood.'

He turned them on the dance floor. The room became a blur of spinning lights and faces to match the jumble of thoughts careening through Jess's head. When she had thought of returning to acting, she'd thought of stage roles. She hadn't seriously expected a small part in a British film to lead to roles in Hollywood. That was for actors who had been to prestigious stage schools, not girls from London's East End who had struggled for each and every role. The best she had hoped for was a job as assistant stage manager at a repertory company.

At least, those had been her thoughts until recently. In the last few months, whenever she thought of life after the war, Milan always seemed to feature.

When they stopped twirling and returned to a steady foxtrot, Jess shook her head and laughed. 'You're having me on. Hollywood eats the likes of me for breakfast.'

'Don't do yourself down.'

'But they wouldn't take me on based on the tiny part I had in a minor British film.'

'British films have done well in America since the start of the war.'

Jess kept waiting for Leo to burst into laughter and tell her it had all been a big joke. She studied his expression. It was deadly serious. 'I'm just an East End girl.'

'The Americans don't know that. To them, you're an English Rose. Think about it. We could be like Gable and Lombard, Olivier and Leigh.'

It only occurred to her after the dance ended and they returned to their table that he had named Hollywood couples rather than individual actors and actresses.

The evening passed in a whirl of laughter and dancing. While Jess managed to dance with some of the other cast members, she found Leo monopolised her. It wasn't like a date with Milan, though. Milan was always interested in what she thought. Her idea of the perfect date had changed dramatically, she realised. Whereas she had always used to dream of an evening just like this, with beautiful dresses, music and dancing, now she couldn't help wishing she was strolling through the woods with Milan, holding hands, talking through everything that had happened since they had last met. Leo, on the other hand, only seemed interested in showing her off, making her feel like nothing more than a pretty ornament. Her shoes still pinched, but when she asked to sit down, Leo insisted on one more dance. It wouldn't have been so bad if it had been a sedate dance, but the band chose that moment to strike up a lively tune, and Leo pulled them into an intricate quickstep.

How she kept a sparkling smile pinned to her face, she didn't know. When the last chord died away, she applauded the band and then returned to her table. She could only pray that Leo wouldn't expect her to dance any more. She thought wistfully of the cosy anteroom in Bentley Manor, and curling up in an armchair in front of the fire, chatting with Evie and May.

A waitress approached Leo. 'There are two gentlemen outside, sir.' The way the girl pronounced gentlemen made it sound as though she thought they were anything but. 'They don't have an invitation but they refuse to leave until they've seen you.' She handed Leo a calling card. 'One of them asked me to give you this.'

Leo glanced at the card. For a brief instant his expression froze, and Jess could swear he turned a shade paler. Then he recovered and gave the waitress a smile. 'It's all right. I'll go and talk to them.'

He turned to Jess. 'Please excuse me. This won't take long.'

The other occupants of the table were all on the dance floor. Jess took the opportunity to ease the tight shoes from her feet under cover of the table. She bit back a groan of relief as she flexed her toes, feeling the blood return to their tips. She didn't mind if Leo spent hours talking with the newcomers; there was no way he was dragging her onto the dance floor again.

The door Leo had disappeared through opened. Fearing it was him already returning, Jess shoved her feet back into her shoes and fled to the ladies' powder room. She gazed at her face in the mirror. 'Chin up, Jess,' she muttered, after a quick glance at the cubicles to make sure she was alone. 'They say you have to suffer for your art.' Pulling her powder compact from her bag, she repaired her makeup, taking as much time as she thought she could get away with before Leo sent someone to look for her. Away from the smoky atmosphere and the loud music, she found herself feeling a flutter of excitement at Leo's assertion that she might land herself work with a Hollywood studio if she played her cards right. She wouldn't contemplate a move to Hollywood – there was no way she would live so far from Hannah – but hadn't Leo intimated some major studios were planning on setting up operations in England? Despite her misgivings about an acting career, she'd be mad to turn down a significant film role, wouldn't she? Anyway, it wasn't as if she had her heart set on a different career.

She seemed to hear Evie saying, 'You can do anything you put your mind to.'

Still, she ought not dismiss anything out of hand. It would be easier to make a decision once she knew exactly what jobs were on offer. As for Leo speaking of them as though they were a couple, it was out of the question, and she would make that clear. She shut her compact with a snap and tucked it back into the beaded handbag. It was high time she returned. She slipped out of the powder room and was about to walk down the passage to the door leading into the club when she heard voices drifting in from an open window.

'I'll get you the money soon, I promise.' That was Leo. His voice lacked its usual self-assurance; in fact, it held a distinct thread of anxiety. Jess's senses tingled.

Another voice spoke. A deep male voice that oozed menace. 'You said that last week.'

'And the week before,' said a third voice that sounded as mean and dangerous as the second.

'I know. I know. Look, I can give you the first instalment on Wednesday.'

'Any reason we should believe you this time?' the second man said. 'Why shouldn't we just make a mess of that pretty face of yours right now?'

'Because I'm coming into big money soon, but I won't get a penny – and neither will you – if you ruin my looks.'

'This is your last chance, Steele. If you don't pay up Wednesday, we're coming for you.'

Chapter Nineteen

'That sounds really bad, Jess. Please say you won't see Leo again.' May's eyes were wide, and her face had turned pale.

It was Christmas Eve and the girls were walking on the common, gathering holly to decorate the anteroom before leaving for the night watch.

Jess regretted letting her love of a good story get the better of her when she had described the mysterious conversation she'd overheard. She should have remembered that May wouldn't see the funny side. Not with her family's involvement with criminal gangs. 'I'll have to see him at the première.' She couldn't deny a thrill at those words: in a few months, she would be attending a première. She would see her name appear on the screen, alongside those of several well-known actors.

Evie cut a long sprig of holly and added it to the pile in her basket. Then she turned to Jess, looking almost as concerned as May. 'But you won't see him alone before then, will you? I agree with May. He doesn't sound like the sort of person you should be mixed up with.'

'Honestly, you shouldn't worry. I'm not mixed up with Leo, as you put it. I'm with Milan, remember.' But as she spoke, she felt as though someone was using one of the holly sprigs to poke her in the back. Being with Leo was like picking at a scab. Although she knew no good would come of it, she couldn't seem to stop herself.

'Are you serious about breaking into film acting, then?' Evie asked.

'I'd be mad to turn down an offer if it came,' Jess said. 'Say what you like about Leo, I'll have a lot to thank him for if he can get me into films.' After a sleepless night spent trying to think of any other job she'd like to do, she'd convinced herself of that.

'If you did, it would be because of your talent, not because of Leo.' May dumped an armful of holly into the basket. Her mouth was turned down in a scowl.

Jess's heart melted. 'May, you're the best friend a girl could have, you and Evie. And you know I take your concerns seriously.'

'Then why do you still go out with him?'

Jess wished she had an adequate answer. Whatever she had once felt for him had died long ago. She loved Hannah too much to regret her birth, and the war somehow made past hurts fade to insignificance in comparison to the terrible things that had happened all around the world. She and Leo had both been different people then.

'Because, like it or not, it helps to know the right people in show business. Leo, for all his faults, is a successful actor. I'd be an idiot to get on his wrong side.' Jess twirled a sprig of holly between her fingers, watching the leaves and the shiny berries merge into a green and red blur.

'I suppose you're right,' May said.

Evie hefted the basket. 'Come on, we've got enough holly to decorate every room in the manor, not just the anteroom.' She looked at Jess with a crooked smile. 'Please don't think we're judging you. If you're sure you're doing the right thing, that's good enough for us.'

Jess smiled back, hoping her smile looked more genuine than it felt. If only she was sure she was doing the right thing. 'Shame acting isn't like the WAAF. I mean, I'd have never believed three working class girls like us would end up officers.'

May gave a relieved smile, and Jess knew she was glad to have avoided an argument. 'Certainly not a girl like me with a father and brother in prison. If it weren't for the WAAF, I don't know what would have happened to me. I would never have got away from my family.'

Jess's stomach twisted at the memory of her own desperation to escape her past. Leo was a permanent reminder of her shameful behaviour, so why did she seem unable to cast him out of her life? The feelings Leo awoke – that she was damaged goods – still made it hard for her to believe that Milan would want her in his life. Surely when Czechoslovakia was liberated, he would return and not miss her.

Hefting her own basket, she gave a bright smile and did her best to push away the gloomy thoughts. 'Come on, let's bring Christmas to the Mess.'

–

The girls were glad of the festive cheer over the days that followed. It made a welcome antidote to the bleak news. The Germans had launched a fierce counter-offensive campaign in the Ardennes, and the Allies had taken heavy casualties. Jess hadn't had a chance to see Milan but knew he would be blaming himself, for part of the problem had been caused by poor weather blocking reconnaissance flights. Although it couldn't possibly be his fault, she knew he would blame himself nonetheless. And every day of delay to the Allied advance was another day added to the occupation of Czechoslovakia.

Together with the cold weather and the short days, January was a grim month. It wasn't until early February that the Allies finally regained the ground they had lost and began the advance again, and the mood became more hopeful.

'Guess what?' Evie cried as she returned from a weekend's leave with Alex in Sussex. 'We're getting married!'

'I could have told you that,' Jess laughed.

'No, I mean we're actually getting married. We've set a date.'

'When?'

'The end of June. The 23rd.'

'But that's ages away.' May said. 'I thought you were going to say it was next week.'

Evie's face clouded. 'I wish it was. But there's so much to organise, what with trying to give my mum and Alex's grandparents enough warning to arrange travel, not to mention getting permission from the RAF. And that's before we've decided who to invite or made my dress. It seemed best to pick a date well in advance.'

'I think it's wonderful news. Congratulations.' Jess was happy for Evie. Really. All the same, she couldn't help feeling wistful at this reminder that both her friends would soon be married. Although things were going well with Milan, he had never spoken of their future together.

'How much leave will you get?' May asked.

'Just a forty-eight-hour pass.'

'For the same days, I hope.'

Evie swatted Jess's arm. 'Idiot. But we're going to wait until the war's over before we apply for a long enough leave together to take a proper honeymoon.'

'But that means you'll be getting married straight after a day on duty,' Jess pointed out. 'What if you're on night watch? We'd have to prop you up at the altar.'

Evie grinned. 'Sounds like I need a couple of bridesmaids. What do you say? One of you can hold my bouquet and the other can hold me upright.'

'I'd love to,' May cried.

'Count me in,' Jess said. And now she found that she was genuinely delighted for Evie. 'After all we've been through together, you don't think I'd let you tie the knot without us to look out for you.'

Evie looked at them both seriously. 'It wouldn't feel right to get married if you weren't there.'

Jess's throat grew tight, and she had to swallow a couple of times before she could speak. 'I'm really happy for you both.' Then she leapt to her feet. 'But what are we doing sitting here? We've got a wedding to plan!'

'Where are you holding the ceremony?' May asked.

Evie gave a mysterious smile. 'Guess.'

'I don't know. Cowley? Here?'

Evie shook her head. 'It's going to be in a place special to all of us.'

'I don't—' Jess broke off as realisation dawned. 'You dark horse! So that's why you went to Sussex.'

Understanding flared in May's eyes. 'Amberton! How perfect.'

Evie nodded. 'We went to see the vicar, and it's all arranged.'

Jess clapped her hands. 'Splendid. I can't wait to see Amberton again. Now, what do you want us to do?'

227

'Can you help me with a dress?'

'Course we can, can't we May?'

A look of panic flitted across May's face but she put on a smile and nodded. 'I'd love to.'

However, once Evie had gone to put her bag in her room, May rounded on Jess. 'How on earth are we supposed to scrounge enough coupons for a wedding dress?'

Jess chewed her lip. 'I know. I didn't want to disappoint her.' She thought of the silk dress Leo had given her, now in its box under her bed. 'You don't know of any way of bleaching a red dress white?'

May snorted. 'Only if you want Evie to walk down the aisle looking like she's just been pulled out of a car crash.'

'Didn't think so. I wonder if her mother's still got her wedding gown.'

But when Evie came back, she shook her head when Jess asked. 'She sold it after the last war. My dad couldn't work for some time and they were short of money.' Evie looked wistful. 'A shame. I've seen photos, and it was really pretty.'

'Auntie Vera's still got hers.' Then Jess grimaced. 'No. It will have been lost in the fire, of course.'

Evie patted Jess's arm. 'Have you heard from your aunt or uncle?'

'I got a letter from Vera yesterday.'

'How is she? And Hannah?'

'Doing well. Hannah's getting on much better with the other children this time. Apparently they're in awe of her now her street's been blown up.' Jess shook her head. 'I'll never understand children.'

'And your uncle?'

Jess stirred, uncomfortably aware that she had neglected Uncle Jack. Between seeing Milan and partying with Leo, all her free time had been taken up. 'Think I ought to visit him on our next evening off. It's a while since I've seen him.' To be honest, she'd been putting it off; visiting Uncle Jack at Mrs Prosser's house would force her to face up to the loss of her childhood home.

'We'll come with you,' said May. 'Won't we, Evie?'

'Course we will.'

'Aren't you going out with Alex?'

'He'll understand. This is more important.'

Jess found herself blinking back tears. 'Have I ever told you how much you two mean to me?'

'Not nearly enough. Now—' Evie turned back to the matter at hand '—what about my wedding gown?'

And the rest of the evening passed in excited chatter as they made plans for Evie's wedding.

–

'Gosh, this is worse than I imagined,' May said as they turned into Farthing Lane.

Jess swallowed to clear the lump in her throat as they passed the blackened ruins where her house had once stood. Evie and May walked on either side, a hand on each arm. Jess appreciated the support. The night the V2 had struck, she had been too frantic with fear for it to sink in that her home was gone for ever. Only now was it starting to dawn on her that life would never be the same again.

'I keep telling myself Hannah, Vera and Jack are safe, and that's the most important thing.' She turned her face from the wreckage and led the way to Mrs Prosser's house.

Mrs Prosser's house hadn't escaped the attack unscathed: all the windows were boarded up, having been blown out in the blast, and even by the fading light of late afternoon, Jess could see cracks in the brickwork. However, it was standing, and that was more than many people could say about their houses in these parts.

Mrs Prosser let them in and exclaimed over the tin of biscuits they had brought. 'Bless you, love. There was no need.' She ushered them into the front room. 'Your Uncle's out in the yard, fetching coal. I'll give 'im a call.'

While they waited, Jess looked around the room. Despite the boarded windows and cracked plaster work, there wasn't a speck of dust anywhere, and the antimacassars were brilliant white. She ran an idle eye along the pictures on the mantelpiece then exclaimed just as the door opened and Jack walked in.

'Uncle Jack,' she said, pointing to a cracked picture frame. 'Your cigarette cards.'

Jack shovelled more coal onto the hissing fire then gave Jess a hug. 'A miracle, it is. I thought I'd lost everything. Then the other day I thought I'd 'ave a poke around the rubble, and I found that – the pride of my collection.' He picked up the frame and held it so May and Evie could see. 'The West Ham team of 1923.'

Evie and May made suitably impressed noises; Jess had to look away, biting back a laugh.

'Well,' Jack went on, replacing the frame with the same care one would take with a newborn baby, 'I knew then everything would be alright. I've got my Vera and our little girl, and I've got my West Ham cards. There's plenty of people who weren't as lucky.'

The door opened and Mrs Prosser came in holding a tea tray. 'That's the spirit, Jack,' she said, evidently having overheard. She turned to Jess. 'You can rest easy, my dear. Your uncle will be fine with me until your aunt comes back.'

'You're very kind,' Jess told her. 'Jack's lucky you and Bert could put him up.'

Mrs Prosser patted her hand. 'I 'ad to do my bit. It's been terrible round 'ere. First the Blitz, then the flying bombs and now these blinkin' V2s. It feels like the end of the world. There's plenty of folk still living in church halls. They've lost everything.'

'I wish there was more we could do to help,' Jess said.

'Bless you, you've done plenty. You're in the WAAF, ain't you? And I'll never forget you and your young man dragging Vera and Hannah out when we'd all given up hope.'

Still, when Jess, Evie and May left, Jess satisfied that Jack was doing well, she couldn't help feeling there was more she could be doing. 'Imagine if Mrs Prosser hadn't been able to put Jack up?' she said as they picked their way with care down the pitch-black streets. 'I can't bear the thought of him sleeping in a cold church hall. Yet plenty of people are living like that.'

'Remember when we took a collection for Coventry at the pantomime?' May said. They had performed the pantomime soon after Coventry had been bombed, and as the evacuees in the village had come from Coventry, they had wanted to do something to help.

'It's too late for a pantomime now,' Jess said. She walked in silence, thinking. 'I suppose we might put on a concert, though. Songs, sketches, that sort of thing. Raise money to buy essentials for the people who are still homeless.'

'That's a great idea. Where would you do it? Here?'

Jess shook her head before remembering her friends couldn't see. 'We wouldn't raise much here. People are rolling in money in Stanmore. We should do it there. We can rope in people from Bentley Priory. There are a couple of choirs. I'm sure they'll want to take part.'

She walked the rest of the way to Bromley underground station with a spring in her step, her head buzzing with ideas.

—

'You will try and come, won't you?' A few days later, Milan had been given a break from duty and had been able to visit again. This gave her the opportunity to ask if he would perform in the concert. The idea had been met with approval by her superiors, and she had been given permission to organise the concert, which was to be held in March at Bernays Memorial Institute in the centre of Stanmore. Several service men and women had already volunteered to take part. If Milan would perform, perhaps accompanied by Kathleen Swift, it would be the crowning moment of her programme.

She gave him her best pleading look. As ever when she looked into his piercing blue eyes, her heart gave a flutter of pleasure. This time, however, it was accompanied by a darker feeling of guilt. Despite Evie's warning, she had allowed Leo to take her out with his acting friends again. Although she made it clear to Leo she was only going as his friend and to take his advice of getting to know people in the film industry, she found Leo's friends and colleagues seemed to assume they were a couple. She didn't want to embarrass him by denying it, so held her tongue.

'I will try,' Milan said, 'but you know it might not be easy.'

Jess bit back her frustration. She was shackled by duty herself, so knew she was being unreasonable by wishing she could spend more time with him. She should be grateful he was based close enough to see her at all when their free days coincided. Maybe it was the lingering worry that Milan couldn't think of her in quite the same way now she had told him about Hannah, but it felt like he wasn't able to get away as often as he had before. It was ridiculous, she knew, yet the niggling feeling that he was making excuses not to see her lingered. It seemed the only time she was able to forget her fears was when she was dancing in a London nightclub, pretending she was an adored film actress. Maybe that was why she never seemed to be able to turn Leo down.

It being a typical February day – cold and drizzly – they went to the cinema in Harrow to see *Blithe Spirit*. Jess couldn't help watching it with the knowledge of what it was like to act in a film, wondering how many times the actors had been required to play each scene. She had watched the credits at the start with a stab of recognition at several familiar names in the crew. Being involved in a film was rather like the feeling of camaraderie she got in the WAAF, she realised. There were dozens of different roles, although most outsiders only knew about the celebrated ones. Yet the people working behind the scenes were just as vital to the whole production. It would fold without everyone playing their part. Perhaps that was why she was drawn to return to acting once she left the WAAF. She wanted to work somewhere that had the same feeling of pulling together to get a job done.

When the newsreel came on, Jess watched the images of ruined towns and villages left behind after the bitter fighting in the Ardennes. She leaned against Milan's shoulder, only belatedly aware that he was tense and shaking. The reason struck her with a sick lurch. 'You think that will happen in Czechoslovakia?' she whispered.

She felt his shoulder lift as he shrugged. 'I cannot say. Czechoslovakia is not in the Allied line of advance. Perhaps there will not be fighting.'

'But you are worried.'

'I am. I worry what the defeated soldiers might do before they leave. Or they might refuse to go. Then there will be fighting, and it will be the citizens of my country who must fight.'

Jess could do nothing but grip his hand, conveying her sympathy and concern through her touch.

'I can only pray it will not be long before I can return.'

There it was again, the feeling that Milan was trying to break away from her. No matter how much she told herself it was her imagination – that he wouldn't carry on seeing her if his affections had cooled – she couldn't shake it off.

They emerged from the cinema to find it was still raining. Now spring was approaching, the last of the light still lingered in the sky. However, it was cold and raining, making walking unpleasant.

'I put my violin in the car,' Milan said. 'I thought we might go to see Kathleen Swift again.'

'She'd like that.' Jess was touched by the concern Milan felt for the grieving antique shop proprietress. She herself had made a point of popping into Stoneleigh and Swift whenever she was passing and Kathleen Swift had been grateful for the companionship.

They found Kathleen just closing the shop, and she greeted Jess and Milan with enthusiasm. 'You couldn't have timed your visit better. My husband was all set for

234

leave, so I baked his favourite jam tarts, and now his leave's been put back.'

'Oh, that's a shame,' said Jess, wiping her wet feet on the doormat as she followed Kathleen inside.

Kathleen locked the door, turned the sign to 'closed' then beckoned them through the shop. 'Come upstairs to the flat. I've just lit a fire, so it's cosier up there.'

She took them to her living room, which was, indeed, warmer than the shop. It was a large room, with pale pink chintz sofas beside the fireplace. In pride of place on the mantelpiece was a photo of a serious looking young man wearing RAF uniform with wings over the breast pocket. Jess knew this must be Daniel, whose violin Milan now carried. The adjacent photograph showed an older man, also in RAF uniform, who could only be Kathleen's husband.

When Kathleen told them that the delicious black-berry jam tarts they had with tea were 'made from blackberries I picked from the common,' Jess and Milan exchanged glances. Jess's insides did a little swoop, and she knew that Milan, like her, was thinking of their autumn walk on the common when they had picked blackberries. Kathleen glanced at the violin case beside Milan's chair. 'Is it too much to hope that you might play for me?'

'Not at all,' said Milan, picking up the case and opening it. 'It would be a pleasure.'

Kathleen disappeared into another room while Milan applied rosin to the bow and tuned the strings. When she came back, she was holding a music stand. 'This was Danny's,' she said. 'You're very welcome to have it.'

Milan thanked her then said, 'What would you like to hear?'

'I don't mind as long as it's something cheerful.'

Milan tucked the violin under his chin and played a tune Jess didn't recognise. She thought it must be another Moravian dance, as it had a similar sound to the others he had played. As she watched him, his lips curved into a smile, his eyes gazing into the distance, fixed, she was sure, on some distant Czechoslovakian scene, she knew with a sudden twist deep in her stomach that she couldn't bear the thought of him leaving her. Yet he had spoken of his yearning to return home, and she couldn't in good conscience ask him not to go when he feared for his sister and nephew's safety. She could only imagine how she would feel not knowing if Vera and Hannah were still alive. With a shudder she recalled the terrifying minutes when she had feared them dead in the rubble of their home. Milan had lived with that fear for nearly six years.

'Oh, that was beautiful,' Kathleen sighed, after Milan had finished playing a selection of tunes. All had been lively, leading his listeners into a world of beauty where war and loss didn't exist. 'You are good to visit me. Life is so dreary and the news so grim, it's hard not to dwell on what I've lost. Your visits always take me out of myself and do me no end of good. I just wish there was something I could do for you in return.'

Milan, his eyebrows raised, indicated the violin he was lovingly returning to the case. 'You have already done so much. I cannot thank you enough for your gift.'

A sudden thought struck Jess. 'Actually, there may be something.' She explained about the fundraising concert. 'You play the piano so beautifully, I wonder if you would like to perform?'

Kathleen coloured, looking pleased. 'You really think I'm good enough?'

Jess opened her mouth to reassure her, but Milan got there first. 'You're very talented. And if I am able to come, I hope you will accompany me?'

Jess took that as an encouraging sign. However, when Milan was walking her back to Bentley Manor, Jess said to him, 'It was kind of you to ask Kathleen to accompany you. Does that mean you'll definitely come?'

'If I can. I cannot yet say for sure.'

It wasn't the definite promise Jess had hoped for. Yet again, it made her wonder if Milan was looking for a way out of the relationship. After all, he now knew that she wasn't good enough for him.

Chapter Twenty

Maybe it was this conviction that Milan was trying to distance himself from her that made Jess unable to refuse invitations from Leo. Whatever the reason, three days later, when Milan sent a message to say he was unable to meet her as promised that weekend, she found herself accepting yet another invitation from Leo. As before, he took her to a nightclub frequented by people from the film world. They hadn't been there long when Leo excused himself to speak to a man Jess didn't recognise. However, judging from the cut of his suit, he was an American, and a wealthy one.

Spying Allan Ford, she went to speak to him.

'Ah, Miss Halloway,' he said as he shook her hand. 'Always a pleasure to see you. You'll be glad to know editing on *Knights of the Skies* is coming along nicely. It's going to be a hit, I can feel it in my bones.' He indicated the grey haired, portly man beside him. 'I don't think you've met Douglas Murray. He's written the film score.'

They shook hands. Then Allan said, 'How are your family, by the way?' He addressed Douglas, 'Jess's family home was hit by a V2 before Christmas.'

Douglas grimaced. 'Terrible business. Friends of mine in Hammersmith lost their home to one of those. They were out when it hit, thank God.'

'My family were saved, too. My aunt and cousin have moved to a relative in Wales until my uncle can rent other accommodation.' Then, deciding she had nothing to lose by asking, plunged on. 'Actually I'm organising a concert to raise funds for Poplar. I don't suppose you'd like to come?' She added the date and location, clenching her hands behind her back to conceal their trembling. She was shocked by her audacity at inviting two such august figures.

'I'll have to get my secretary to check my diary, but I would love to come,' Douglas replied.

Jess decided this meant he was too polite to turn her down flat. 'Well, it would be wonderful to see you if you can make it,' she said, with every expectation that his secretary would discover an engagement he couldn't wriggle out of.

'In fact,' Douglas added, 'do you have room for more performers? I'd be happy to play a piece on the piano, if that would help.'

Jess had to resist the urge to pinch herself. 'I... that would be amazing. I can't thank you enough.'

'Not at all. And if you need them, why not ask Allan here to ask around the actors he knows to see if any are available to perform a short scene?'

'Of course. Anything I can do to help.' Jess thought the director didn't look quite so enthusiastic, but she wasn't going to turn down any offer, no matter how half-hearted.

'Excellent.' Douglas clapped Allan on the back. 'Well, no time like the present. There are plenty of people here we can ask. Anything to help the future Mrs Steele.'

'I... what?' But Douglas had already dragged Allan in the direction of a doyenne of the theatre, whom Jess had been longing to speak to but hadn't dared. Now, however, all thought of meeting one of her heroines fled. She marched towards Leo, who had now finished his conversation with the important American.

'Why are people talking as though we're engaged?' As irate as she was, she was aware of eyes upon her and made sure she fixed a smile to her face.

Leo's face dropped. 'Come and dance. We can talk without being overheard.'

This wasn't the outright denial she had wanted. However, she held back her sharp retort until they were gliding across the dance floor to 'A Nightingale Sang in Berkeley Square'.

'You'd better have a jolly good explanation,' she hissed. 'You know I'm seeing someone else.'

'Yes, a Czech pilot who will no doubt return home the moment the war is over.'

She swallowed. 'Even if he does, what makes you think I'd want to marry you? We're not together.'

'We were once. We were good together.'

'You took advantage of me.'

'It takes two to tango, my darling,' he said. 'I don't remember you complaining.'

That hurt almost as much as the reminder that Milan would soon go home to Czechoslovakia. 'Maybe I didn't,' she said. 'But just because I made a mistake once, when I didn't understand what I was doing, why do you think I would make an even bigger mistake now I see you for the Lothario you are?'

Leo remained silent while he steered them around a corner. From the beaming smile on his face, no one would have guessed they were in the middle of an argument. Jess had to hand it to him, he was a pretty good actor.

'Look,' he said after a move that brought them along-side the band, 'It doesn't have to mean anything.'

'What do you mean?'

Leo sighed. 'The thing is, you know I mentioned having a Hollywood studio interested?'

Jess nodded.

'Well, they were rather lukewarm until they saw that photo of us in the paper. Remember the one?'

'If you're talking about the one that led to me being given the third degree by my friends and boyfriend, then yes.'

'It made the studio take notice. They loved the idea of selling them the romance of a British acting couple.'

Jess missed a step then stumbled over Leo's foot as she tried to catch up. 'Are you trying to tell me all that talk of joining a Hollywood studio was as your wife?'

Leo's shifty expression was all the answer she required. Jess gave a nod of the head towards the other women in the room. 'I suggest you take your pick from one of the actresses who actually care about you. If I ever get work with a Hollywood studio it will be through my hard work and talent, not because of some fake marriage.' She had never been more impatient for a dance to end. She wasn't usually lost for words, but Leo's bare-faced cheek left her groping for a strong enough insult.

'At least think about it,' Leo said. 'Don't sacrifice a great career just for the sake of your pride.'

'Whose career – yours or mine?'

'Both, of course. Think about it. You're not getting any younger. Do you seriously think you could make it on your own?'

'I'm twenty-four!'

'That's old by Hollywood standards.'

Jess trod on Leo's foot again. This time it wasn't an accident, and she took great satisfaction in the brief wince he gave before he smoothed over his expression with a beaming smile. 'If you don't tell your American friends it's no deal, I will.'

'All right, then. Just don't deny it until I've signed with them. Don't spoil my chance just because you're too much of a goody two shoes to go along with it.'

'No! My boyfriend was already upset by that photo. I won't do anything else to hurt him.'

A crease appeared between Leo's brows. They danced for the next few bars in silence. Then he said, 'I hear you've managed to persuade Douglas Murray to help out with your little fundraising event. How would you feel if I told him the concert was just a front to make money for yourself? I'm a good enough actor to be able to plant doubt in his mind.'

'You wouldn't.'

'Whereas,' Leo continued, 'if you allowed the studio to believe we were a couple, I could round up a few of my actor friends to put on a show. I'm sure my name would draw far more people than you would get for an amateurish show put on by WAAFs.'

'How dare you use other people's misfortune for your own gain?'

'It's your decision.'

Jess ground her teeth, struggling to think of a way out. Finally she said, 'Very well. I won't deny it but neither will I confirm it if asked.' Any threat to herself she would have ignored. However, the families who had lost everything needed as much money as could be raised. She wasn't going to let her pride prevent them getting the help they needed.

She would just have to make sure she told Milan before he found out from another source. He would not be pleased.

–

Milan flung himself into a chair in the anteroom of the Officers' Mess and rubbed his eyes. He had flown deep into Germany today to photograph possible sites where V2s were being produced. There had been residential areas nearby, and Milan tried not to think about the possible results if RAF Intelligence decided to launch an attack. There was always the fear that he had assisted in a raid that would result in civilian deaths. There were times when he missed the days of the Battle of Britain, when it had been a case of shooting down an enemy plane before you got shot down yourself. Not that he really wanted to return to the days when it had looked as though Britain, too, would be invaded, but at least he hadn't felt complicit in civilian deaths.

He ordered a cup of tea and was halfway through it before he noticed Jiří sitting in a quiet corner, doing nothing but turning a pocket watch over and over in his hands. Milan knew Jiří had inherited it from his grand-father, and it was the only possession he'd been able to take out of Czechoslovakia. Merely the fact that Jiří was alone and not in the middle of a crowd, joking about his latest scrape, alerted Milan that something was wrong. He picked up his cup and went to sit next to his friend.

'What has happened?' he asked. He spoke in Czech as he always did when alone with Jiří. As the war had progressed, there were fewer men he could speak to in his mother tongue, so he always took every opportunity to speak Czech, enjoying having no need to grope for words and, most of all, the reminder of home. It also meant in this case that they would be less likely to be interrupted.

Jiří turned bloodshot eyes upon him. 'You have not heard?'

'Heard what?' A cold chill ran through Milan. Jiří had remained light-hearted throughout the Battle of Britain, when they had faced death every day and seen friends shot down in flames. What could make his friend look so grief-stricken now, when victory seemed just around the corner?

'Praha,' Jiří said – Prague. He managed to inject a lifetime of grief and despair into those two syllables. 'It has been bombed.'

Milan's mouth went dry. Then he shook his head as he thought about it. 'Are you sure? It doesn't make sense. Why would the Nazis bomb Prague when they occupy it?'

'I am sure. I met Jan Dvořak today. You know, the one who works at Fursecroft.' Jiří named the London building occupied by the Czech government in exile. He drew a shaky breath. 'It was not the Germans. It was the Americans.'

'Impossible!'

Jiří closed his hands around his watch, his knuckles turning white. He shook his head. 'It is true. Jan told me. It was a mistake. They don't understand how it happened, but the Americans lost the navigation beam. They thought they were bombing Dresden when really...' His voice tailed off.

Milan looked at him in horror. Prague was not so very far from Dresden. A bomber flight coming from Britain would only need to be off by a small angle to find themselves over Prague by mistake. He swallowed. Dear God, please don't let this be true. Eliška and Franta lived on the outskirts of Prague. 'Do they know which areas were hit?' Horrific images flooded his mind. He saw again the devastation caused by the V2 at Jess's home, only this time it was not the brick terrace that had been flattened but the pretty terracotta tiled houses of his hometown.

'I... I do not remember every place they named,' Jiří said. 'I am sure they did not mention Roztoky, though. I would have remembered.'

Milan relaxed a little, grateful that his friend had spared his own family a thought even through his own worry. How the Czech government in exile had got their information he didn't ask. They had their own chain of communication to their homeland, and it was best not to know too much about it.

Jiří continued, and now Milan had to strain to hear, for Jiří's voice was scarcely more than a whisper. 'But Vyšehrad was hit.'

'Jiří. I am so sorry.' Milan forgot his fears for his own family in his concern for his friend. Vyšehrad – the Prague district that had grown up beside ancient ramparts high above the east bank of the Vltava – was where Jiří had lived. All his family lived there.

Jiří turned his white face to Milan, his expression fierce. 'I have to go back.'

'Jiří, you know that's impossible.'

'It's not. If the information got through to the government-in-exile, we can get to Prague.'

Milan's stomach tightened at Jiří's implication that Milan would join him in his madness. Not that the same thought hadn't occurred to him over the years, especially after the news had reached them of the reprisals following

Heydrich's assassination. 'Jiří, see sense. You can't just leave your post.'

'Why not? My family needs me.'

Milan sighed and told Jiří exactly what he had told himself when news had broke of the massacres following Operation Anthropoid. It was cruel but had to be said. 'The best way you can help them is by staying here and doing your job. Even if you could get through to Prague, you wouldn't get there in time to help anyone who was caught in the bombings. You must trust the people around them to care for them if they need help. There is nothing you can do except play your part in ending the war.' He paused, waiting for a response. When none came, he added, 'You know I'm right.'

Jiří gazed at his hands in silence for several long seconds. Then he turned his pain-ravaged face to Milan. 'When the war ends, will you come with me?'

Milan nodded. 'I will. We will leave no stone unturned until we have found our families.'

Jiří grasped Milan's hand. 'You promise?'

Milan couldn't help a fleeting thought of Jess. What would she say to him leaving for Czechoslovakia at the earliest opportunity? While his common sense told him she would understand – she knew how it felt to fear for one's family, after all – he wondered if she would wait for him if he left her for an unspecified length of time. Still, he had no choice. He needed to know what had happened to Eliška and Franta, and he would do all he could to help Jiří. 'I promise,' he said.

It was only later that it occurred to him that he had, without realising it, pictured a future that didn't lie in Czechoslovakia. A future with Jess in England. What would Jess think? She seemed fixed on acting, and now spent more time with Leonard Steele and her acting friends than she did with him. Even if she did choose him, how would he support her once he left the RAF? Before he had always pushed such thoughts out of his mind, not daring to believe he would survive the war. Now, as the Allies advanced ever closer to Berlin, he knew he could not put off such decisions for ever.

He would request leave for the concert, he decided. He rarely took leave, having nowhere to spend it, so he doubted he would have trouble getting his request granted. He would use the occasion to try to work out whether he and Jess had a future.

Chapter Twenty-One

Jess burst into the anteroom, carrying a large parcel which she had just collected from the post office. Seeing Evie and May in chairs beside the fire, she made a beeline for them. 'It's arrived!' She put the parcel on the floor then dropped onto her knees on the rug and tugged at the twine that held the lid securely onto the box.

'What is it?' asked Evie, gazing curiously at the box.

'A present from Mrs Grey.'

May gave an excited squeal. 'Is it what I think it is?'

'I hope so.'

Evie looked from May to Jess. 'Are either of you going to let me in on your secret?'

'Patience!' Jess freed the last knot with a sigh of relief and unwound the string from the box. Then she eased off the lid. Inside was the dress they had made out of parachute silk for the pantomime. Jess had worn it when playing Cinderella.

She held it up with a flourish for Evie to see. 'You shall go to the ball, Evie Bishop! What do you think? We're about the same size, so it should fit. There are several underskirts to make it stand out, but if you'd rather go for a sleeker look, we can remove them. That would give a load of fabric to make long sleeves.'

Jess was gabbling rather, as Evie hadn't said a word. Instead, her eyes had filled with tears. Jess gazed at her in dismay. 'If you don't like it, there's so much spare fabric, we could make up a new dress to a completely different pattern.'

Evie shook her head, pulled out her handkerchief and dabbed away the tears. 'Don't be silly. This is perfect. You're a genius, Jess.' She stood and took the dress from Jess, holding it up against herself. 'I can't believe this is really happening. I'm going to marry Alex!'

She pulled Jess and May into a three-way hug. 'Thank you both. I thought I was going to have to get married in my uniform.'

'Well that would have been the something blue sorted,' Jess said, hugging Evie back.

Evie looked at the dress. 'I suppose this would count both as the something old and the something borrowed.'

'No, wait. Come upstairs. I've got the perfect something borrowed.' Jess led them up to their room. She reached under the bed and pulled out the box containing the silver and gold peep-toe sandals Leo had given her. 'Go on. Try these on with the dress. I want to see how they look together. Then we'll decide on any alterations.'

Evie stripped off her uniform and, with Jess and May's help, eased the dress over her head. Jess pulled up the zip then stepped back to look. The sweetheart neckline and tight fitting bodice showed off Evie's slender waist to perfection. Her red hair seemed to glow a deep bronze against the white parachute silk. The skirts billowed around her. Evie beamed at her friends in the mirror. 'I don't want you to change a thing. I really will feel like I'm marrying my Prince Charming now!'

Evie's feet were a little smaller than Jess's, so the sandals, which had pinched Jess's feet, fitted Evie perfectly.

'You can keep them,' Jess said. 'They'll never fit me properly. Then they can be the something old and the dress will be something borrowed.'

'Are you sure?' Evie raised the hem of the gown to admire the knotted gold and silver straps around her feet. 'I can't keep these.' She met Jess's gaze in the mirror and gave a wicked grin. 'I'll spend the whole day swooning over these instead of Alex.'

Jess grinned back. 'Seeing as every time you're together, you usually trip over your own feet because you're too busy gazing at him to look where you're going, I'll consider that an improvement.'

'What about your something new?' May asked.

Evie sighed. 'Unless I want to get married in my ancient WAAF blackouts, it'll have to be new underwear. Goodness knows where I'll find anything pretty.'

'We'll find something. Some of the shops are getting more things in from America now.'

The dress had been made in a very short time; some of the seams had ripped and when Jess made Evie stand on a chair so she and May could inspect the hem, they noticed that the hem lay slightly lower on the left.

'It didn't matter in the pantomime,' Jess said, taking a pincushion from her sewing box and pinning the hem. 'No one would have been looking at it carefully enough to notice a crooked hem. There's no way we're going to let you walk down the aisle in a lopsided gown, though.'

Finally, when they had made a note of everything that needed mending or adjusting, Evie removed the dress with a reluctant sigh. 'I wish I could wear that all the time.'

'It'd get in the way something terrible in the Filter Room,' Jess told her, picturing the billowing skirts sweeping all the tracks from the table whenever Evie turned. She took out a large coat hanger from the wardrobe and used it to hang the gown on the back of the door.

Evie sank on her bed looking suddenly wistful. 'Alex has found a cottage to rent right here in Stanmore. I'm going to apply to live out.'

'But that's wonderful.' May sat on the bed beside Evie. 'There's no reason you'd be turned down, is there? Why the long face?'

Jess did her best to hide her feelings behind a smile while Evie seemed to grope for words. 'It is wonderful. I can't wait to show you the cottage. It's beautiful. It's one of the houses in the row at Little Common.' Jess knew the houses Evie meant. They were more like part of a country village than a London suburb. The cottages were clustered around the edge of a pretty pond.

Jess turned abruptly, making a show of straightening the gown on its hanger. She'd had plenty of time to get used to the idea of her friends marrying, but right now her throat ached, and she didn't trust herself to speak without her voice cracking.

Thankfully, Evie and May didn't seem to have noticed anything wrong. 'I suppose it's all happening so fast,' Evie said.

Jess found the power to turn with what she hoped was a twinkling smile. 'Fast? You've been engaged for years. I was beginning to think you didn't want to get married.'

As soon as she saw Evie's expression, Jess wished she could take back her words. She had meant them to be gently teasing. Instead they had spat out like machine gun fire. She sighed and flopped onto her own bed. 'I'm sorry. That came out all wrong. I'm happy for you, Evie. I really am. I just suppose I'm not quite ready to lose you.'

'Lose me?' Evie came to sit next to Jess. 'Jessica Josephine Jane, that's the most ridiculous thing I've ever heard.'

Despite herself, Jess felt a reluctant smile tug at the corner of her mouth. 'I don't suppose either of you are ever going to forget my full name, are you?'

'No chance,' Evie said. 'But we promise only to use it when you've said or done something particularly thick-headed.'

'That's all the time, then,' said Jess with a grimace. 'There are times I really don't know how either of you can put up with me.'

Evie and May exchanged a worried glance. 'What's got into you?' Evie took Jess's hand. 'Jess, you're the truest friend anyone could have. You've stood with us through thick and thin. You don't think either May or me are going to let that go after we get married? What kind of friends do you take us for?'

Jess's throat felt so thick she could scarcely force out the words. 'You don't know what I was like. Before the war.' A strange buzzing sounded in her ears. She had put off this moment far too long, telling herself she could wait just another day and then another until weeks had passed since she had resolved to tell her friends the truth. But she couldn't bear hearing Evie's promise that nothing would change knowing that everything would change if only they knew.

May leant forward, her face creased with concern. 'We know what you're like now and we love you for it. I don't think you can have been much different before we knew you.'

'And of course things will change,' Evie went on with a nod to May, 'but you don't think we're planning on leaving you behind, do you? I can't imagine a life without you. It's as unthinkable as a life without Alex or—' she seemed to grope for another piece of her life she couldn't bear to be without '—or maths,' she finished with a triumphant smile.

Despite herself, Jess snorted. 'I'm flattered. Better not let your mum know she comes somewhere behind maths, though.'

Evie eyed Jess keenly with a gaze that made Jess feel distinctly uncomfortable. 'My mum knows she means the world to me. You, on the other hand, seem to be particularly dense this afternoon. What have I got to say to make you see sense?'

Jess shrugged, unable to meet Evie's eye. Her secret was a relentless pressure in her chest. She didn't want to hide it from her friends any longer, yet neither could she bear the thought of losing them. Evie was still holding Jess's hand and now she squeezed it. 'I don't know what more I can say. Except that if, once I've got my maths degree from Oxford and possibly a PhD as well, Alex and I decide to start a family, I can't think of anyone I'd rather have for a godmother than you.' She gave a little nod to May. 'And May, of course, but she doesn't seem to be suffering the same loss of sense as you today.'

It was as though the effort of concealment had finally caught up with her. Her ears filled with a buzzing noise. This couldn't be happening. She was Jess the flirt, the confident girl who always had a cheery quip on her lips and who breezed into a room bringing sparkle and glamour. She didn't dissolve into tears when a friend told her how much her friendship meant.

Unfortunately, her body didn't seem to have got the message. She pulled her hand free from Evie's and covered her face when her mouth started to quiver. Much to her horror, a sob welled up from her lungs and burst from her throat. The look of shock and dismay on Evie and May's faces would have made her laugh if she wasn't so busy trying to suppress the tears that now poured down her cheeks.

'Jess, what on earth is the matter?' Evie's face creased with concern. 'Is it Milan? Has something happened?'

All Jess could do was shake her head, unable to get any words out through the sobs that heaved from her lungs. She took the handkerchief that May handed to her and wiped her eyes. It was May's round-eyed look of fear that helped her control her breathing and force out a few words. 'Milan's fine. It's me. You won't want to be friends when you know.'

'How can you say that?' Evie rubbed Jess's shoulders.

There was no concealing it any longer. Evie and May had shown such confidence in her. She couldn't let them go on believing a lie any longer. It took several minutes to control her sobs enough to get any coherent words out. In the meantime, Evie and May hovered over her, patting her shoulders in the same manner someone would approach an unexploded bomb.

Finally she spoke. 'I'm sorry I hid this from you.' She blotted fresh tears with the hanky. 'I know you won't feel the same way about me when you know. And I won't blame you.'

'Know what?' May asked.

Jess drew a shaky breath. The only way to do it was get it out quickly. Milan hadn't abandoned her, and she drew hope from that. 'Hannah isn't my cousin. She's my daughter.'

Evie and May exchanged glances again. Then Evie took Jess's hand, still clenched around the handkerchief, and patted it. 'We wondered how long it would take to get you to confess.'

'I… what?' If Evie had announced she was going to leave the WAAF to become a chimney sweep, Jess couldn't have been more flummoxed. She looked from one to the other of her friends. 'Didn't you hear what I said?'

Evie gave Jess what could only be described as a pitying look. 'If you think we can be your closest friends for five years and not realise that you're hiding what you regard as a deep, dark secret then you're insulting our intelligence.'

Jess gazed back uncomprehending. 'You mean you already knew about Hannah?'

'We weren't certain, but we had a pretty good idea. It was clear you were avoiding taking us to meet your family, and it was also clear you were so ashamed about something you thought we'd leave you high and dry if we found out. It didn't take much effort to work out what it was.'

'If it's any comfort, we weren't sure until just now,' May added.

'I suppose you can tell me who the father is an' all.'

Evie said, 'Seeing as you looked like you wanted to curl up in shame when you told us about Leo, I assume it's him.'

'Good grief, can't a girl have any secrets?' Jess could hardly take in what she was hearing. Ever since Leo had turned up, she had lived under a tremendous weight of dread that her friends would discover her secret and disown her. Now it turned out she was so transparent, everyone knew. 'Why didn't you say something?'

'You seemed so ashamed. We thought you'd feel worse if you knew what we were thinking. Besides, we were just guessing. It's not the kind of thing you ask a person.'

'I suppose not.' Jess studied her fingernails for a moment. Then: 'And you still want to be my friend?' She cringed at her tone. She sounded like a lonely child pleading to be playmates. Maybe it wasn't much different.

'Of course we do,' May said. 'I thought we were best friends. Best friends don't abandon each other just because they made a mistake.'

First Milan and now her friends. It seemed she had seriously underestimated them. Jess swallowed to ease her aching throat before saying, 'Sorry for not having more faith in you. I just couldn't face seeing the disgust in your eyes.'

'It's only natural to be afraid,' Evie said.

'Yeah, but it would have saved me a whole agony of worry.'

'What about Milan. Have you told him?'

Jess nodded. 'I told him right after he hauled Vera and Hannah out of the wreckage. He was fine about it too.' She dabbed the last of the tears from her cheeks with a shaky hand. If only she'd confided in Evie and May before, she'd have been saved all this dread.

'That's wonderful,' May said. 'There's nothing to worry about.'

Evie, however, was chewing her lower lip. She leaned closer to Jess, her expression serious. 'Why do you keep seeing Leonard Steele? He's bad news.'

'How many times do I have to tell you? He can help my career.'

Evie leaned back shaking her head. 'I don't buy it. You want to know what I think?'

'Do I get a choice?'

A ghost of a smile appeared on Evie's face. 'Not really.' She looked away for a moment as though marshalling her thoughts, then took a breath and met Jess's gaze. 'Has it occurred to you that you are trying to punish yourself?'

'Why on earth would I—?'

Evie held up a hand to stop Jess's protests. 'Hear me out. You've got a wonderful chap who is crazy about you and, judging from the way your whole face seems to glow whenever he's around, you're head over heels in love with him. Yet, unaccountably, you keep him at arm's length all the time you're both at Amberton and give him the push for no real reason when you get transferred.'

Jess shifted position while Evie spoke then shifted again. The mattress was lumpy, and she couldn't seem to get comfortable. 'You blew hot and cold with Alex,' she couldn't resist saying.

'True. And I nearly lost him because of it. I'm trying to stop you from making the same mistake.'

Jess could see nothing was going to stop Evie saying her piece. She might as well hear her out. 'Go on, then.' She knew she sounded like a petulant child; it was all she could do not to fold her arms and stick out her lower lip.

'Very well.' Evie gave Jess an understanding smile. For some reason it only served to annoy Jess more. 'So you are free to spend time with as many men as you like during the four years you're apart, yet although you go on a few dates, you never see any man more than two or three times. You never let them get serious about you because you know you could never regard them as anything other than a bit of fun to pass the time. You say it's because you don't want to get tied down. Whereas we—' Evie inclined her head towards May '—know it's because you can't bear to spend too much time with any man who isn't Milan.'

Jess shifted again. She'd never noticed before how uncomfortable her mattress was. 'You're very sure of yourself.'

'I happen to know you extremely well.'

'Do go on,' Jess said with mock politeness. 'I'm dying to know what happens next.'

'So after over four years apart, you and Milan meet up. And suddenly, even though you've said all along that you don't want to get involved with anyone, you are spending as much time together as you're able.' Evie paused, her gaze going distant. 'You know that feeling when you're looking at a complete tangle of an equation, and you can't see how to solve it? Then you suddenly realise you can take out a factor to make sense of the whole thing?'

'No.'

Evie batted aside Jess's denial with a negligent wave. 'Anyway, that's how it felt to me, seeing you after you'd met up with Milan again. It was so obvious that you truly loved him. That was why, although you were always talking about meeting pilots, you never allowed yourself to get serious with any of them. But then Leonard Steele appeared on the scene.'

Jess's stomach gave an uncomfortable lurch. She really didn't want to talk about Leo now Evie and May both knew exactly what part he had played in her past. It was one thing to know her friends accepted her, mistakes and all, but to hear those mistakes discussed was too much.

Nothing could stop Evie when she was working through a particularly thorny problem, however, and she seemed to be treating Jess's behaviour as just another complex equation that needed solving. All Jess could do was let her get on with it.

'We couldn't work out why, although you obviously preferred Milan, you were prepared to risk Milan's feelings by carrying on seeing Leonard,' Evie continued. 'Both May and I had noticed that you seemed to be ashamed of something in your past. And before you accuse us of discussing you behind your back,' she said when Jess scowled and drew breath to speak, 'We tried to bring up the subject a couple of times, yet you brushed us off.'

Jess subsided and started to pick at a loose thread on the blanket. She wished she could shut out Evie's voice but there was no escaping it.

'I think you're punishing yourself,' Evie said.

'So you said. You haven't managed to convince me, though. Care to enlighten me?'

'It's obvious, isn't it.' Evie addressed Jess in patient tones as though she were explaining to a child that two and two made four. 'Deep down, you think you're not good enough for Milan. Neither of us—' here she gave another tilt of the head towards May '—think that's true, of course. We happen to think the world of you.'

Jess swallowed. The buzzing in her ears had started up again. What was wrong with her that a few kind words could set her off like this? 'I… you don't know what you're talking about,' she said.

'Think about it. It makes sense. You love Milan so you can't stay away from him, yet you think you're not good enough for him so you punish yourself by hanging around the bloke who reminds you of your past. It's nothing to do with your career.'

It was all too much to absorb. The relief of her friends' acceptance and the fact they had guessed the truth all along had set her mind in a whirl. She couldn't cope with delving into the strange hold Leo seemed to have on her. Not yet.

She sprang to her feet on legs that felt suddenly shaky. 'I don't know. I can't think. Anyway, I ain't got time for this. It's only a week till the concert, and I've got to go and—' she racked her brains for a plausible excuse '—check that the room is ready.'

She took one step towards the door then stopped when May clutched her arm. 'Think about it,' May said. 'We're here when you're ready.'

With May's face shimmering through unshed tears and her throat aching, Jess could only nod. She managed to make it to a quiet corner of the garden before being overcome by tears of relief and gratitude.

Chapter Twenty-Two

There was a buzz of excitement in the air in the days leading up to the concert. On March the seventh, Allied troops crossed the Rhine, and the feeling was that the Nazi resistance couldn't hold out much longer. Although V2s continued to fall, more and more launch sites were being captured, thanks in large part to the work of the women in the Filter Room, using information fed to them by their sister Filter Room workers who had been taken to Belgium to pinpoint launch sites. While the Filter Room was still busy, Jess didn't feel the same sense of despair that had haunted her when the V2s had started falling. Now she knew that every launch site they helped destroy could no longer be replaced by troops in retreat. They were winning the war in the air and on the ground. It could only be a matter of time before it was all over.

Despite the excitement, she couldn't stop thinking about Evie's theory. No matter how outrageous her suggestion had been, Jess found it impossible to shake off the nagging suspicion that Evie might be right.

'Ridiculous,' she said out loud as she arranged chairs into rows in the Memorial Hall. It was the morning of the concert, and she had requested a forty-eight-hour pass to prepare.

'What is ridiculous?' asked a voice.

Jess jumped and spun round, pressing a hand to her chest. There was Milan, holding his violin. 'Milan! I didn't hear you come in.' Standing on tiptoe, she kissed his cheek. Before she could step back, he pulled her close and planted a lingering kiss on her lips. For a brief moment, all her worries melted away, and she allowed herself to relax. While she was in Milan's arms, she could believe they had a future together.

'I'm so glad you're here,' she said.

'I told you I would do my best.' While he had met with Kathleen Swift to rehearse the piece he had chosen to play, he hadn't been able to guarantee his attendance until just three days earlier.

Jess stepped back to look at him properly. He looked tired, she realised. His face was pale, as though he had spent too much time cooped up indoors – or in the cockpit of an aeroplane – and there were fresh lines around his mouth and eyes. Lines of strain. 'Is everything all right?' she asked.

He nodded. 'I have been busy. That is all.'

She hesitated. 'Have you heard any more about Jiří's family?' She had listened in shock when Milan had told her about the mistake that had led to a bomber flight bombing Prague instead of Dresden. Her heart had gone out to Jiří, knowing how helpless he must feel not knowing if his family were safe or not.

'Not a thing. I do not think there is any way of knowing for sure without going there.' Milan tugged at the knot of his tie as though it were too tight. 'Jess, I must speak to you about—'

'Actually, I must speak to you, too.' Jess was acutely aware that Leo and some of the cast and crew from the film would be arriving soon, and she needed to tell Milan about her arrangement with Leo. They had only met once since Leo's confession about the fake marriage, when Milan had been so troubled about the Prague bombing, she hadn't wanted to add to his worries. Although they had spoken on the telephone several times, it hadn't been a conversation she'd wanted the operator to overhear.

She swallowed. If she was honest with herself, she had put off telling Milan because she knew how weak it made her sound. 'Leo's coming this evening.'

A slight frown had furrowed Milan's brow. Now it cleared. 'You do not have to worry. I know having him here means you will raise more money.'

Hell's bells. Why had she waited this long to tell him? His understanding made it all the worse. She moved another chair, taking great care to line up the legs with the one to its right. 'There's something else, though.' She kept her eyes on the chair while she spoke. 'He's pretending that we're getting married so he can get work with a Hollywood studio.'

Milan burst out laughing. Jess was so surprised and relieved, she dropped the next chair she had just picked up. 'What will they say if they sign him and discover you have no intention of marrying him?'

Jess released a shaky breath and grinned at Milan. 'I don't think he's thought it through. He's just desperate to get work.' Then a memory returned. 'Actually, I think he's found himself in debt to the wrong people.' She repeated the conversation she had overheard at the Christmas party.

She moved to pick up another chair, but Milan placed his hand over hers, stopping her. 'I understand you want to raise money. I would go to any lengths to help the people of Prague. If there was anything I could do.' Jess could feel the full weight of his helplessness and frustration in those last words. She had the impression Milan was talking to himself, his gaze focused on a scene a thousand miles away. Then he seemed to recover himself and he was seeing her again. 'I will not bother telling you I do not like it. You are not an idiot. You know how this makes me feel.'

Jess almost wished he would be angry. Tell her she had to refuse to cooperate with Leo's lies or he would leave her. This patient understanding only made her feel worse. A mental image flashed into her mind of Evie giving her a knowing look. 'See,' she seemed to say. 'You're punishing yourself.' She swallowed and opened her mouth to speak but Milan went on.

'I do not wish to see you hurt. And this man still has the power to hurt you, I think.'

Jess had no answer to that. She moved more chairs in silence. Milan helped her. She was grateful that now he had made his position clear, he did not labour the point. Whenever she looked at him, he seemed lost in thought.

Then she remembered that he had been about to tell her something earlier. 'What did you want to say to me?' she asked.

But the door swung open again, and Evie and May appeared, having just finished their shift in the Filter Room. And there was no chance to find out what Milan had wanted to say. Still, there would be plenty of time after the concert.

–

Seeing Evie and May arrive, Milan slipped away into a back room to warm up before the concert. After tuning his violin, he ran through a series of scales and arpeggios.

His mind drifted while his fingers automatically worked through the familiar exercises. It had taken all his self-possession not to show Jess how hurt he was that she could allow another man to pretend they were together. Did that mean he could not put his arm round her or hold her hand while Leo and his friends were in the room?

He supposed he was partly at fault. He had pursued Jess doggedly at the start of their relationship then when they had met again he had fought to keep seeing her. Yet now, several months afterwards, he hadn't spoken up. Hadn't so much as hinted that he saw any future with her. He supposed with Evie's wedding fast approaching and May and Peter clearly also destined for marriage, Jess must be expecting Milan to speak up and ask her to marry him. However, despite knowing he wanted a future with her, he didn't know what he had to offer her. His life was in Prague. Thanks to his new violin and the improvement he had seen since starting to practise again, he was hopeful of finding work in an orchestra or even as a soloist in Prague. He had already made something of a name for himself there, and hopefully he would be able to pick up his life again if he returned. No one knew him in London. He didn't think he would find it so easy to make a life for himself here. Until he knew what he was going to do, he didn't feel it was fair to burden Jess with his feelings. And without declaring his intentions, he felt he had no right to complain if she saw other men. He hoped Leonard Steele didn't hurt her, though. He had used her and discarded her once before, and Milan hadn't seen any sign that he was sorry for the way he had treated her back then.

After playing through the piece he planned to play later, he left his violin and returned to Jess. The room was filling up when he emerged from the side door into the hall. There was a buzz of excitement among the audience.

'Is it true Leonard Steele will be performing?' he heard one middle-aged woman say to another. Both sat near the front and wore what Milan guessed was their Sunday best dresses and hats, their hair expertly waved and their faces made up with almost as much care as Jess's. Both craned their necks to look at the entrance each time the door creaked open, and Milan knew they were straining to catch a glimpse of Leonard Steele.

He turned when a hand slipped through his arm and saw Jess, her eyes alight. 'Isn't it marvellous?' she said. 'Look how many people have turned up already.'

'That's thanks to you and all your hard work.' And her contacts in the acting world.

Jess led him to a group of chairs at the side of the hall. 'The performers will sit here,' she said. 'I've put Douglas Murray and Leo's group as the last acts.' She leaned closer with a grin. 'It'll make sure everyone stays until the end,' she added. 'I've put you down to play third, because I know you'll really make the audience sit up and take interest after a couple of air force choirs who, between you and me, aren't bad but nothing special.'

The door opened again, and Milan could tell from the ripple of interest from all those already present that it must be Leonard Steele arriving. Jess hurried to greet him, and Milan drew several slow, deliberate breaths to calm the sudden flare of temper. When Jess returned, she was accompanied by four men. There was no mistaking the famous face of Leonard Steele among them.

Jess introduced him, her smile a fraction too bright and her voice a shade higher than usual. Milan would have much rather punched him in the face than shake his hand, but he didn't want to embarrass Jess. Besides, it wouldn't do to injure his fingers. He contented himself with gripping Leonard's hand until he spied a flicker of discomfort in the man's eyes.

Although Jess also introduced the other three men, Milan didn't pay attention to their names, and he quickly forgot them. His head was too full of anger towards the self-satisfied Leonard Steele who right now had his hand on Jess's shoulder and whispered into her ear. Milan only unclenched his jaw when Jess stepped away from Leonard, shot Milan an apologetic smile and disappeared backstage.

Soon the hall filled up. Jess walked on stage in front of the curtain and the hum of conversation died down. Milan's heart gave a leap, as it always did whenever he saw her. 'Ladies and gentlemen, welcome to this concert in aid of the victims of the V2 bombing in Poplar. All proceeds from the ticket sales will go towards providing for the families who lost their homes and possessions during the attack. We've got some wonderful acts lined up for you tonight, so without further ado, I'd like to welcome onto the stage the barbershop quartet, Air Fours.'

The curtains opened to reveal four young RAF officers who, Milan supposed, must be attached to RAF Bentley Priory. Despite Jess's warning, they were rather better than Milan had expected and after singing three songs, left the stage to enthusiastic applause. Milan took the opportunity to slip through the side door and he went to collect his violin. After checking it was still in tune, he carried it into the wings and watched a group of WAAFs perform a lively rendition of 'Chattanooga Choo Choo'. Looking out across the audience he saw smiles and heads nodding to the beat, indicating people were enjoying the first two performances far more than Jess had estimated. He could only hope that the piece he had decided to play wouldn't prove too highbrow and spoil the mood.

It was amusing to watch the audience. More than one woman surreptitiously leaned forward or back and kept turning their heads to dart glances at the group at the side of the hall then quickly turned their faces back to the stage before their companions noticed. Usually their companions were too busy doing the same thing to notice where their neighbours were looking.

On stage, the WAAFs reached the end of their song with a flourish and the audience applauded. The young women trooped off, blowing kisses to the audience, and Jess strode back onto the stage to introduce him.

'Thank you, Waaflers,' she said. 'And now I'd like to introduce you to a talented violinist who will be playing "Havanaise" by Saint-Saëns, accompanied by Mrs Kathleen Swift. Please give a huge welcome to Milan Mašek.'

Milan walked onto the stage, his sleeve brushing Jess's as she headed for the wings. He couldn't help it. He smiled at her, happy to see her in her element, organising an event to help others. Jess's face was turned away from the audience as they passed. She shot Milan a glare, giving an unmistakable nod of the head towards the side of the hall where Leonard Steele sat. *Don't spoil this for me*, her look said.

Milan could keep his feelings in check just as well as Jess. Even while he bowed to the audience with a polite smile plastered to his face, his eyes sought out Leonard Steele and silently promised retribution to the man who had treated Jess so badly yet expected her help in furthering his career.

He tucked the violin under his chin then gave Kathleen a nod. The first gentle chords of the piano sounded then Milan was playing the lilting first notes. Even though Jess wouldn't allow him to display his true feelings for her in public, she couldn't prevent him from pouring all those feelings into his playing. As his fingers ran up and down the strings, he forgot everything except the emotions of the past few months. His love for Jess, his fears for his family, the hollow in his heart from being exiled from the country he loved. He found expression for them all in this piece of music that alternated between dreamy, drawn out notes and explosive bursts of furious bowing as his fingers moved faster than thought. At these moments he attacked the strings with all the savagery he longed to inflict on Leonard Steele.

Before he knew it, he had reached the final drawn out high notes. He looked into the wings and met Jess's gaze, feeling like he had experienced a catharsis. Somewhere in the storm of music, his thoughts had fallen into place. He knew what he had to do.

After the final note faded into silence a hush fell on the hall. The audience was so still, Milan could hear the blood pulsing in his ears. Then someone coughed; that seemed to release everyone from their spell, and the audience burst into enthusiastic applause. Milan took a bow then walked into the wings.

As he passed Jess, she caught his sleeve. 'That was…' She shook her head wordlessly and dabbed at her eyes. She gave a crooked smile. 'Good job you're only playing once, or I'd lose all my mascara.' After a brief squeeze of his arm, she walked onto the stage.

He didn't hear what she said to the audience. He walked straight to the room where he had left his music and violin case and packed it away. Then he picked it up and walked out into the passage leading to the hall. He nearly ran into a distinguished looking man in late middle age.

The man took Milan's hand and shook it vigorously. 'Splendid performance,' he said. 'Takes me back to hearing that piece performed by Yehudi Menuin.' Then he fumbled in his pocket. 'I'd love to talk to you, but I've got my own performance to prepare for, and I've got to dash off at the end. Another engagement, you know.' Milan, his thoughts still in turmoil after his performance couldn't really take in what was happening. He just nodded and muttered something in reply, he hardly knew what. Then the man pulled something from his pocket and handed it to him. Milan saw it was the man's card. The name 'Douglas Murray' was printed on it in elegant copperplate. It rang a bell, but Milan wasn't able to place it. 'I'd very much like to talk to you,' Douglas Murray said. 'Get in touch when you have a moment.'

Milan nodded, scarcely taking in what Murray had said. He put the card in his pocket and then he was heading for the hall to the door while Murray went backstage.

He pushed the encounter to the back of his mind as he took his seat. His head was too full of Jess to spare a thought for anyone else.

The decision that had occurred to him on stage remained unchanged. He needed to give her time. If she truly loved him, she would not toy with his affections. He would tell her what he had decided after the concert.

Chapter Twenty-Three

Jess watched the two acts following Milan in a daze. She had chosen well to place him third in the billing. A large proportion of the audience had only come to see Leo, so putting a star performer that early on had made people sit up and take notice. Fewer people had been watching Leo while Milan played – Milan had grabbed their attention.

Jess had known he was an accomplished violinist but somehow, seeing him play for an audience, she knew she was seeing him in his element for the first time. It was something of a wake-up call. She'd only known him as a fighter pilot. Although she'd known he must have had a different life in Czechoslovakia, it was only seeing him come to life on stage and pour his spirit into his performance that she recognised his true calling. A deep sorrow twisted her at the fresh realisation of what the war had taken from him.

Jess emerged from her daze in time to see Kathleen finish her solo to loud applause. She watched her friend take her bow with warmth swelling in her chest. She was so pleased for Kathleen to see her taking more interest in life again. Although the loss of her son would be a grief she never truly recovered from, Jess hoped she would be able to be more engaged with the world from now on and reconnect with her friends. She beamed at Kathleen

271

as they passed each other on the stage and was rewarded by a broad grin in return.

The rest of the concert passed in a blur. It was a huge success, and the audience loved every minute of it. Jess was secretly pleased that although Douglas Murray gave a brilliant rendition of a Chopin piano solo, he didn't get more applause than Milan. Of course, the moment the whole audience had been waiting for was Leonard Steele's act. He, together with two other members of the RAF Film Unit sang 'Three Little Maids' from the Mikado, complete with much coy fluttering of fans and surprisingly tuneful high-pitched voices. The audience gave them a standing ovation as they minced off the stage, Leo blowing kisses to the women in the audience over the top of his fan.

Jess wiped tears of laughter from her eyes as she walked back out onto the stage to thank everyone and announce the final total raised. She had just finished speaking when she was surprised to see Leo stride onto the stage holding a huge bouquet of flowers. 'One last thank you before we all leave,' he said, speaking in a carrying voice that easily reached the back of the crowded hall. 'I can't let you all go without asking everyone to show their appreciation for this wonderful young lady who organised the whole thing and has given us such a delightful evening.'

Even as Jess acknowledged the applause and admired the flowers, she couldn't help a stab of resentment at the proprietorial way he referred to the show. He spoke as though he had been one of the organisers instead of simply turning up to perform his act.

Leonard held up his hands; the applause died down. 'I also can't let you go without making an announcement I've been dying to share with the world for some time.

Ladies and gentlemen, I'm so proud and delighted to announce my engagement to this beautiful woman. Jess Halloway has consented to become Mrs Leonard Steele.'

Jess felt the blood drain from her face. A sort of happy sigh seemed to surge through the audience, and a ripple of applause broke out. A bright light flashed, making spots of colour dance in front of her eyes. So that was why he had been so eager to take part in the concert. Not because he felt the slightest bit of concern for the poor people who had lost their homes but so that he could ambush her with this announcement. Another flash of light. It took a moment for her to work out that it must have been a photographer. Leo had clearly tipped off a reporter. It was that realisation that brought the power of movement back to her limbs. She was nearly overcome with the urge to beat Leo over the head with her bouquet. That would give the reporter something to write about. However, while it would be satisfying in the short term, she knew that humiliating a well-known actor in front of the press would not endear her to the very people she would need to impress should she try to pick up her acting career after the war. The image of her beating Leo over the head until he was covered in petals and the bouquet was reduced to bare stalks was so strong, a mad urge to laugh welled up inside her. She used it to turn a beaming smile upon the audience. A fraction of a second later, a third flash dazzled her. When the blotches in front of her eyes cleared, most of the audience was a blur. The only faces that stood out were the worried ones of Evie, May, Alex and Peter and the stony expression of Milan's.

A hush fell over the audience, and she knew everyone was waiting for her to say something.

Leo put an arm around her shoulders. 'Look at her. She's so shocked, she doesn't know what to say. She begged me not to make a fuss, but I couldn't resist.'

This wasn't entirely true. She had a few choice words she would love to say. However, saying them in such a public way would result in her being hauled in front of her CO, charged with actions unbecoming to an officer. She couldn't see the reporter but knew he must be there, pen poised to take down every word she said. It gave her an idea.

Her face aching from maintaining her smile, she turned to Leo but pitched her voice for the audience to hear. 'I only asked you not to make a fuss because I didn't want anyone to forget the real reason for the show, which is to raise money for the victims of the bombings. And even though he asked me to keep it secret, I'm sure he won't mind me saying that Leo—' she turned to the audience with a self-deprecating smile as though embarrassed by her slip at referring to Leo in such a familiar way '—I mean, Leonard Steele, has agreed to donate the generous sum of one hundred pounds to the cause. I asked for a donation in place of an engagement ring.'

The audience gave a murmur of approval and another ripple of applause filled the hall. Jess turned back to Leo and felt a stab of satisfaction at the flicker of alarm in his eyes. He controlled his expression immediately and turned a fond smile to the audience. 'That's the girl I'm going to marry. Isn't she wonderful?'

After yet more applause, Jess said to the audience. 'Thank you all for coming and for raising money for such an important cause.'

There was a buzz of chatter and the scraping of chairs as people rose and fumbled with coats and hats. Jess dragged

Leo to the side of the stage. The moment they were out of sight, she rounded on him. 'How dare you? I have friends in the audience. My superior officers. Milan's here. Did it ever occur to you to consider how your clever little stunt would affect me?'

'You'll sort it out.' Now they weren't being watched, Leo's smile disappeared to be replaced by a scowl. 'And if you were going to lecture me on pulling stunts, you should have done it before pulling one on me. How selfish can you get?'

'Selfish? If I was being selfish, I would have demanded the ring as well. Imagine what a good story that would have made for you, not only making the donation but buying me the perfect sapphire ring.'

Leo acted like he hadn't heard her. 'You know I was having money problems, yet I can't back out. Imagine the bad publicity.'

'Bad publicity? I'll give you bad publicity. The next time you try ambushing me, just remember how interested the press would be to meet your six-year-old daughter.'

The shock on Leo's face brought her to herself. What had she done? She'd sworn never to breathe a word of Hannah's existence to Leo.

Leo's expression twisted into a sneer. 'You're lying. If this is an attempt to wangle more money out of me, you can forget it.'

Jess forced a smile. 'Course I am. You can't blame a girl for trying. Now get out of my way. I need to see my friends and start undoing the damage you've caused.'

She pushed past him and marched back out onto the stage and down the steps. From the corner of her eye, she saw Evie and May approach. Yet they could wait. She pushed past the members of the audience who were still lingering, probably hoping for a last glimpse of Leo. She remembered to fix the smile back on her face and gave them polite nods when they called out their congratulations. She hardly glanced in their direction, though. All her attention was focused on Milan. Please don't let him have gone already.

Then she saw him. He had moved aside to let people past but he showed no sign of leaving. His greatcoat was still draped over the back of his chair and the violin under his seat. Some of her fear eased as she hurried over. If he was going to leave without speaking to her, he would have done it already.

'I swear I had no idea Leo was going to do that,' she said the moment she was close enough to speak without being overheard.

'He is using you,' Milan said. 'I warned you he would do something like this.'

'I know.' She folded her arms, hugging her stomach in a futile attempt to ease the knot of anxiety. After a quick glance behind her to make sure no one was within earshot, she lowered her voice and said, 'That's not the worst of it, though. I was so angry with him I let slip about Hannah.'

Milan's eyes widened. 'What did he say?'

'He thought I was lying. Trying to force more money out of him. I didn't correct him.' She glanced over her shoulder again, schooling her face into a calm expression to make it appear she was simply thanking Milan for taking part. 'But what if he thinks it over and wonders if I was telling the truth?'

Milan squeezed her arm. 'What can he do? Even if he sees Hannah, he cannot be sure she is his.'

Jess reeled as though she had been slapped. 'You… you think there was someone else apart from Leo?'

'What? No. That is not what I meant.'

'Then what did you mean?' Jess felt her anger flare up. 'Because it sounded to me like you thought Leo might not be the father.'

Aware that her indignation had caused her to raise her voice, she looked round again only to see the hall was empty. She had arranged to meet Evie, May and their respective boyfriends at the Abercorn; clearly they had already gone on. 'Come on,' she said. 'The janitor must be waiting to lock up.' She went to fetch her greatcoat.

'Jess, you know I believe you. I meant Hannah looks nothing like Leo. She looks like you.' Milan offered her his arm as they made their way through the dark streets to the Abercorn. Jess was tempted to ignore it then slipped her hand into the crook of his elbow, not wishing to appear churlish. Besides, dark clouds covered the night sky, making it dangerous to walk without taking extra care. She knew she had overreacted to Milan's clumsy comment but she couldn't seem to shake off the hurt it had caused.

'I know. Ignore me. I'm angry with Leo, not you.'

'I will not ignore you, either. How can I ignore the fact that I have the most beautiful woman in the world with me?'

Jess spared him a smile even though she knew he wouldn't be able to see it. 'Thank you.' After a few more steps she remembered their earlier conversation. 'There was something you wanted to say to me before.'

She heard Milan give a heavy sigh. 'It is not good timing. It can wait.'

'No. I've gone on about myself all evening. It's your turn.'

Silence for a few more steps, then: 'I do not want you to take this the wrong way.'

'How will I know what the right way is unless you tell me?'

'Very well. I have already told you that Jiří's family live in the area of Prague that was bombed?'

Jess nodded before remembering he could not see her. 'Yes. How is he taking it?'

'Not well.'

'I'm sorry. Tell him I'm thinking of him, won't you?' She had always been fond of Jiří and it broke her heart to think of the young man being unable to get word of his family to discover if they were even still alive.

'I will. But listen. The war will be over soon. A matter of weeks now, they say. I have promised Jiří I will go to Prague with him as soon as we are able. He must look for his family and I must find mine. We will support each other.'

Jess clutched Milan's arm feeling suddenly light-headed. 'When are you coming back?'

'I do not know. Travel will not be easy. I will do my best to return when I can.'

'Of course.' Jess felt sick. He was lining up his excuses, she was sure of it. He had been looking for a way out ever since he had found out about Hannah. It was why he had never spoken of their future together. How ironic when, after she had been the one to hold back from a commitment and make Milan do the chasing, he was now trying to end it with her. He would do it gently, she knew, because he was a kind man. He would go to Prague. Then would come the letter saying his sister needed him and he must stay longer in Czechoslovakia. He would suggest she shouldn't wait for him because it wouldn't be fair on her. He would sound regretful when really she knew it would be a relief. Because she was damaged goods.

Chapter Twenty-Four

As the weeks went on, spring arrived in full force. The days grew longer and sunnier so the girls were able to enjoy the gardens at Hill House once more. Although they were still busy in the Filter Room, the flights they were tracking were friendly. No V2s had fallen since March. While the atmosphere in the Filter Room could never be described as relaxed, the tense buzz of the days of flying bombs and V2s was absent. As each day passed with no enemy aircraft it became more evident that Germany had now retreated beyond even the range of V2s.

'It looks like you might be having a peacetime wedding,' May said to Evie one afternoon. It was late April, and the warm sunshine and gentle breeze had beckoned them out of doors on their free day. They had gone for a walk on the common and wandered through glades carpeted with bluebells, breathing deeply to take in their soapy-sweet scent and gazing up at the blue sky through the fresh green haze of newly unfurled leaves. Finally, they had retreated to Brewers Ponds – the large pool at the southern edge of the common – and sprawled on the bank. As she listened to the tapping of woodpeckers and the soporific cooing of wood pigeons, Jess had a sense of the weight of six years of war lifting from her shoulders. As May implied, the feeling was that the war would be over in a matter of days. Every day the papers carried fresh news of the latest city to be liberated.

'I hope so.' Evie plucked a long strand of grass and twirled it between her fingers. 'I mean, with Alex working in Intelligence, there isn't the same worry as when he was flying, but I'm glad it looks like we'll be married in peacetime. It feels like a more propitious start to our marriage, somehow.'

As ever, when Evie spoke of Alex her face lit with a soft smile. Jess couldn't help smiling back at the sight of her friend so happy.

However, Jess's happiness at the prospect of an end to hostilities was more complicated. As every day brought them a step closer to peace, Jess felt a growing weight on her heart. Soon Milan would be free to return to Czechoslovakia. The closer they came to their parting, the more Jess knew she didn't want him to leave.

–

Two days later the girls came into the anteroom at Bentley Manor to find the other off-duty officers gathered around Laura Morgan.

'What's happening?' Jess asked as she joined the group.

Laura Morgan turned to face Jess, her eyes shining. 'It's been announced on German radio that Hitler has died in action. I've just got in from the Filter Room, and the Controller heard it direct from the Air Vice Marshall.'

'No way,' Jess breathed. 'Then it really is all over.'

'Not quite. Dönitz is president now, and he hasn't surrendered yet. They think he will announce it soon, though.'

After so many months of watching what had felt like the Allies' agonisingly slow advance across Europe since D-Day, everything seemed to happen very fast after that. Two days later, Dönitz announced Germany's surrender, and German troops around Europe laid down their arms. The officers of No. 2 WAAF Officers' Mess got into the habit of having the radio on low in the anteroom throughout broadcasting hours, waiting for an announcement they were sure must come soon. Then late in the evening on May the 7th, the radio programme was interrupted with a news flash, announcing that the war in Europe was over. The next day would be Victory in Europe Day, a public holiday.

Spontaneous cheers rang so loudly in the anteroom that the glasses, cups and saucers upon the tables rattled. Suddenly everyone was laughing and hugging. Laura Morgan went to the ancient gramophone and put on a record. Glenn Miller's 'In The Mood' blared across the room.

Jess grabbed Evie's arm in her right hand and May's in her left and dragged them into an impromptu dance. Other women were hugging, cheering and dancing.

'I can't believe it's over at last.' Evie pulled Jess and May into a hug when the music came to an end.

'I know. It's…' Jess searched for words. She should be happy. She *was* happy. But she couldn't feel the same euphoria the other women displayed.

'I don't suppose Leonard Steele wants to join the party?' one of the girls asked Jess, looking hopeful.

Jess managed a smile and shook her head. She had tried explaining to the other WAAFs that Leo had overstepped the mark with his public announcement, but no one believed her.

'She's just being coy,' Laura Morgan cried. 'Promise you'll remember us when you're rich and famous, drinking champagne every day.'

Through the cheers and laughter, the sound of a horn tooting outside provided a welcome relief. She crossed to the window and was about to carefully peer out without letting any light escape when she suddenly realised there was no need for the blackout any more. She flung back the curtains and saw Peter in his car.

'Come here, May. It's Peter.'

May gave a cry and ran out. A moment later, she was in Peter's arms.

Jess turned away, although before she could rejoin the dancing, Evie grabbed her arm with a cry and pointed out of the window. 'Look! He's proposing!'

Jess spun round and saw Peter now on one knee in front of May who had pressed her hand to her mouth. The couple were bathed in golden light shining from the windows, although the light couldn't compete with the glow of happiness on May's face.

Despite her happiness for May, she couldn't help a twinge of envy. While the end of the war meant her friends could finally marry, it brought only separation for her and Milan. She supposed he would be leaving soon, although the reports she'd received said that there was still fighting in Prague. The weight that had lifted with the news of victory settled back over her heart. He would go, and she knew he wouldn't be back. He would return to his former life and forget about Jess. After all, who would want to be mixed up with a woman who had a child that was not his?

Then May turned and must have seen them looking through the window, for she beckoned them to join her and Peter.

There were tears in May's eyes as she pulled Evie and Jess into a three-way hug. 'I'm so happy,' she said. 'Peter's asked me to set a date for the wedding.'

'That's wonderful!' Jess did her best to push aside her sadness over Milan. No one deserved happiness more than May, and Jess didn't want anything to cloud the celebrations.

'Have you decided when?' Evie asked.

'Not yet. As soon as we can, though.' May shot Peter a glance and blushed. 'We've waited five years. I don't want to wait any longer.'

It was impossible to begrudge May her joy, and Jess joined the merrymaking as enthusiastically as the others.

However, the next afternoon, when they came off watch, Jess felt the need to lift her spirits. 'Let's go into London,' she said. 'I want to join the party.'

Her hopes of celebrating with just the girls were scuppered when she saw Peter and Alex waiting for them outside Bentley Manor. 'You didna think we were going to miss the fun?' Alex said. 'Come on. I'll give us all a lift into town.'

The streets were crowded, and Alex was hardly able to drive faster than walking pace in places, as the pavements were thronged with revellers, all waving at every passing vehicle. It was impossible to remain gloomy while watching such an explosion of joy, and Jess waved back with exuberance, leaning out of the car window. While the car was stopped to let some people cross the road, a girl of about ten ran up and handed Jess a flag through the window. Jess cheered, waving the Union Jack at all the passers-by.

Finally, Alex announced that the crowds were too thick to get much further by car. By this time they were driving down the Edgware Road. He turned off and parked on Seymour Place. 'We can walk from here,' he said.

'Where are we going?' May asked as she clambered out of the back seat and took Peter's arm.

'Buckingham Palace,' Jess said. 'It's the only place to be at a time like this. Come on. We'll walk through Hyde Park.'

They walked back onto the Edgware Road. They had paused to cross when Jess caught sight of a tall man in RAF uniform approaching them.

'Isn't that Milan?' Evie asked, pointing.

Jess's heart gave an odd thump. It didn't seem possible, but there was no mistaking Milan's dark good looks. She felt pinned to the spot, and it was up to Evie to wave and beckon him over.

'What are you doing here?' Evie asked.

Milan pointed up the road. 'Visiting the Czechoslovakian bookshop.' Jess was convinced that wasn't the whole truth. For starters, he wasn't carrying any books. This wasn't the place to ask, however.

She was struck that this could be her last chance to see him before he returned home. Feeling as though her throat was being tightly squeezed, she invited him to join them. She felt a flutter of joy when he agreed and walked by her side. Her hand on his arm, Jess was able to forget they would soon be parted.

They strolled through the crowds, all of whom seemed to be heading in the same direction. They walked to Marble Arch then into Hyde Park.

'At least we've got space to move in here,' May said.

'You'd better brace yourself then,' Jess told her with a grin. 'People will be packed like sardines in front of the palace.'

They soon found Jess was right. They cut first through Hyde Park then Green Park and came out on The Mall. The large space in front of the palace gates was a sea of people. Some waved flags and streamers, others wore red, white and blue hats.

Evie stood on tiptoe, gazing towards the palace. 'I can't see a thing,' she said. Jess, too, found herself unable to see over the sea of heads and soon gave up because it was impossible to stand on tiptoe when being jostled by so many people.

'What about you, May? What can you see? There are times I wish I was as tall as you.' She had to raise her voice to be heard over the cheering crowd.

'You wouldn't when it comes to making clothes.' May leaned on Peter's arm to steady herself. 'I can't see anyone on the balcony,' she said at last. 'I thought the king would be there.' She sounded disappointed. 'Oh, look!'

'What at? The only thing I can see is the back of this bloke's jacket. I—' Jess broke off with a little scream as strong arms hoisted her into the air. All she could do was clutch her hat to stop it falling off as the crowds and the sky spun in front of her eyes. Then she was sitting on Milan's shoulders, her skirt rucked up, his hands on her thighs to steady her. In the moment it took her to catch her breath, she congratulated herself for wearing her best silk stockings. Imagine if he'd put his hands on her legs only to encounter thick lisle!

From her perch she could see clear across the heads and waving flags to Buckingham Palace. As May had said, the balcony was empty. 'None of the royals are outside yet but they're bound to come out soon,' she called down.

'But how will we see anything when they do?' Evie craned her neck to peer up at Jess.

Jess pointed across to the tall monument, topped, appropriately enough, by the bronze Winged Victory. 'Let's climb up there.' She tapped Milan's hand. 'You can put me down now.'

Once back on the ground, she slipped her hand into Milan's feeling slightly woozy. She could still feel the warm imprint of his hands on her legs.

Although there were others upon the memorial, there was plenty of space. The six of them climbed the steps and managed to find a spot that afforded them a clear view to the palace. Milan managed to wedge himself up on a plinth beside a bronze statue of a woman and a lion. Jess climbed up beside him and reckoned that standing in the secure circle of Milan's arms, she had the best view of the palace.

The crowd were chanting, 'We want the king!' over and over. Evie and Alex, May and Peter, standing on the steps below them, took up the chant. Then Jess joined in. Only Milan remained silent. Jess supposed that seeing the royals couldn't be the same for him.

All of a sudden, cheering broke out in the parts of the crowd closest to the palace gates. People were pointing at the balcony, and those holding flags waved them furiously; streaking the air with a red, white and blue blur. Jess leaned forward, holding Milan's arms for support. Then she saw it: movement as the balcony door swung open. Figures stepped out. Jess counted four. Although it was too far away to see their features, Jess knew she was seeing King George, the queen and the two princesses.

Watching the royal family waving at the crowd, and the scenes of jubilation all around her, Jess became more and more aware of Milan's stillness. She tightened her grip on his arms, and he hugged her in return. This was no place for any conversation, however much she might want to ask him why he didn't seem to be joining in with the celebrations. Although on reflection, she supposed it wasn't a surprise. All around them people were expressing their joy that the war was over and they had survived. But Jess couldn't help thinking of those who didn't have much to celebrate. Those whose loved ones weren't there to celebrate with them, those who had suffered life-changing injuries, those who had lost their homes. And elsewhere in the world, the war was still raging. Even in Europe, the war wasn't completely over. For people like Milan, who had been away from their homeland for years, there was the uncertainty of going home, not knowing if their loved ones would still be alive to celebrate with them. Funny that Milan had wanted to join the celebrations at all, now she came to think about it.

After the royal family left the balcony, Jess had the urge to move on. 'Come on. Let's walk up to Trafalgar Square. I want to see what's happening up there.' By this time the sun was setting. Although Trafalgar Square was only a little over half a mile from Buckingham Palace, it took them over an hour to get there. All the way up The Mall, people would drag them into impromptu dances. Complete strangers would dash up to Alex, Peter and Milan, seize their hands and shake them vigorously, thanking the 'brave lads' for their courage in the skies. No one thanked her, Evie or May, Jess thought a little sourly. It was as though people really did believe the WAAFs were just stationed at RAF bases for decoration, just as in the first version of *Knights of the Skies*.

The base of Nelson's Column was clad in fresh hoardings. It was growing dark now, and searchlights had been directed onto the square and played up and down the column. 'Victory over Germany 1945,' read one side of the hoardings. Another urged revellers to: 'Give thanks by saving.' Hardly had they arrived when a conga line straggled past. Jess found herself grasped around the waist and carried into the line. Immediately she reached for Milan and pulled him with her. She leaned forward and shouted into his ear, 'I don't want us to get separated.' Looking around she saw Evie, Alex, May and Peter also being drawn into the dance. The roaring of the revellers battered her ears, she blinked each time a searchlight flashed across her face. With each pass of the lights across the crowd she saw people frozen in a moment in time. There were faces wreathed in smiles, raised arms waving flags and couples entwined. She was in a crowd of strangers, yet no one felt like a stranger. They had all suffered through the same privations, faced danger together. At that moment she would have said they were all one family. Tired as she was after a full day on duty, she wouldn't have missed this for the world.

Eventually her throbbing feet wouldn't allow her to dance another step. They were passing St Martin in the Fields church, so Jess broke free from the line and, keeping hold of Milan's hand, made a dash for the portico. She sank onto the steps; Milan sat beside her and wrapped an arm around her shoulder. Where they were positioned, beside one of the tall pillars, they were in complete darkness. For a while they sat watching the celebrations without speaking. It looked as though the party would be going on at least until dawn.

Now they were not in the thick of the revelry, the noise wasn't so overpowering. She leaned her head against Milan's shoulder. 'Funny. I hadn't expected to see you today.' Her voice was a little hoarse after all the shouting and singing. It was a relief to speak at a more normal volume. 'How come you were on the Edgware Road? The real reason. Don't give me that line about buying books.'

Milan sighed. 'I was not going to tell you today.'

Suddenly she felt cold. She had unbuttoned her tunic but now she pulled it around her. 'Tell me what?'

'I went to Fursecroft.'

Fursecroft. It took a moment for Jess to make the connection. When she did, it felt as though a lead weight had hit her stomach. Fursecroft was the house where the Czech government-in-exile had set up their main offices. She remembered now that it was located on one of the side streets just off Edgware Road. She licked dry lips. 'Why?'

'I told you I promised Jiří I would go back with him as soon as possible. I went to see if there was a transport that would take us to Prague.'

'And is there?'

'No. They told me I must wait.'

The surge of relief was followed by guilt. Milan was desperate to find his family. It was selfish of her to want him to stay.

'I will find a way, though. Soon. I promised Jiří.'

It sounded so final. Was his promise to Jiří more important than staying with her? Tears pricked her eyelids.

She was glad of the darkness. It meant he would not see her cry.

No. She wouldn't cry, even though no one could see. She had brought this on herself. There was no point in letting him know she wished he would stay when he had made up his mind to go. To put distance between himself and the young woman he'd got involved with before he'd discovered she was unworthy of his love. While he might have told her he didn't blame her, that his sister's experience made him understanding of her plight, Jess knew he couldn't really want to get involved with her. She was the fun one. The one men flirted with before going on to marry good girls like Evie and May.

Sparkle. Don't let him see how much she was hurting.

She rose, ignoring her aching feet and back. She grasped his hand and pulled him to his feet. 'Come on, then. If this is the last time I see you, we have to make this a night to remember.'

'Jess, I—'

But she gave him a swift kiss then dragged him back into the crowd of rowdy merrymakers. She didn't want to hear him say goodbye. On this night of victory, she wanted to pretend they would be together forever.

Chapter Twenty-Five

'Jess!' Milan wanted to ask what she meant, but the noise of the crowd made conversation impossible. Did she think he wouldn't return for her?

A couple of people in the crowd sang the opening lines of 'We'll Meet Again', and everyone else picked it up, belting out the song with tears in their eyes. Tonight, the lyrics held less of a feel of imminent parting and instead were full of triumphant promise.

Milan pulled Jess into his arms. In the crush, there wasn't room to dance, but they swayed on the spot in time with the music. Putting his lips close to her ear, he said, 'I will return.'

She shook her head with a sad smile that made his breath catch. Pulling his head down so she could speak into his ear, she said, 'You don't have to pretend.'

'I'm not, I—'

'Please. Let's just enjoy tonight. I know you're leaving. You don't have to explain.' Then she kissed him. He breathed in the familiar floral scent he always associated with her and tasted salt on her lips. He didn't care that they were in the middle of a cheering crowd. Holding her close, so close he could feel her rapid heartbeat against his chest, he poured all the words he was unable to speak into the kiss.

When they finally separated, he saw Evie and May pushing towards them. They were beckoning, so they forced their way to the edge of the crowd, where it was possible to hear them.

'Alex says it's time to leave,' Evie said in a hoarse voice. She and May immediately moved away.

Milan took Jess's hand, intending to walk with her, but Jess put a hand on his chest. 'No. We need to say goodbye.'

'I will phone tomorrow to—'

'No.' One of the searchlights briefly caught Jess's face, and Milan saw the glint of tears.

His confusion changed to cold dread. 'Jess, you cannot mean this.' Once before she had broken off their relationship; he couldn't bear to lose her again. 'I don't understand. I love you. I thought you loved me.'

'I do. I—' Her voice cracked. For the briefest moment, her face crumpled. But then she drew a breath, straightened her shoulders and looked him in the eye. 'You need to find your family, and we both know what we have isn't strong enough to bring you back.' Her mouth trembled, and she pressed her lips together tightly.

Milan seized his chance to say, 'I *will* return. I promise. I love you.'

Jess recovered and shook her head. 'Don't give me false hope. It's been fun, but I know it can't last. Let's finish on a high note.'

She leaned towards him as though about to kiss him. Then she stopped. 'Goodbye.' Her voice was husky, as though her throat was too tight to force out more than that single, heartbreaking word. An instant later she turned and moved to follow Evie and May.

'Jess, wait. Please.' Milan reached for her hand, but it slid through his grasp and she was gone.

The days passed with Milan too heavy-hearted to join in the celebrations of his comrades. He had tried several times to phone Jess, but she had not taken any of his calls. He briefly considered speaking to Evie or May, then decided Jess wouldn't welcome them discussing her behind her back. The final blow came when he sent a letter and it was returned unopened. He had to accept that she truly meant her goodbye. He couldn't understand it. He had believed her when she said she loved him. The only conclusion he could reach was that the lure of a career in films had proved too powerful and she had decided to go ahead with the sham marriage after all.

On the fifth morning after VE Day, he reluctantly decided to turn his thoughts to his family. Just as he was planning another trip to the Czechoslovak government-in-exile, he was summoned to a briefing. Wondering what on earth he was expected to photograph now the Germans had surrendered, he collected his kit. When he clambered into the Humber that would take him to the Intelligence Room, he saw Jiří was already inside.

'So you have been summoned too,' he said to his friend.

Jiří nodded. 'Any idea what this is about? I thought all missions would have finished.'

They found out when the briefing started. 'Intelligence have requested information on German troop movements,' their commanding officer told them. 'They need to see if the surrender is proceeding according to agreement. The two of you will take a Mosquito to photograph troop positions in Germany.' He went on to list a series of targets, finishing with, 'And your final target is here, just outside Dresden.' Milan looked at the map and the germ of an idea formed. It was madness, he knew, but it buzzed around his head and refused to be ignored.

He held his silence until they were airborne, not daring to speak in case someone overheard. It was only when he could see the glistening ribbon of the Channel below them that he finally put his thoughts into words.

'Dresden is not so far from Prague,' he said, adjusting his oxygen mask which vibrated against his face as he spoke into it. He twisted in his seat, glancing back at Jiří, sitting in the navigator's seat behind him. From force of habit, he scanned the skies for enemy fighters. Then it struck him with an odd sense of dislocation that there would be no enemy fighters in the skies ever again.

He couldn't see much of Jiří's face beneath his mask apart from his eyes, which seemed to glint even brighter than the sunlight on the sea.

'You want to fly over Prague?'

While they usually spoke English when flying missions together, now they both spoke Czech. It seemed only natural.

'I can do better than that. I think we're due for a little engine trouble, don't you?'

Jiří's voice went an octave higher. 'You're going to land?'

'Only if you agree.' Milan shot another glance at Jiří. 'What do you say? Fancy a trip to Prague?'

'I thought *I* was the mad one.' This was muttered under Jiří's breath, and Milan wasn't sure if he'd heard correctly, but Jiří's wide eyes spoke volumes.

'I promised to come to Prague with you.'

'Yes. *After* leaving the RAF.'

Milan shrugged. 'If you haven't got the guts…'

'I didn't say no. I just… let me think.'

'You've got until Dresden.'

They didn't say much after that, apart from Jiří's instructions to keep Milan on course. It was a good thing there weren't any enemy aircraft to evade, because Milan was too busy thinking about the possibility of seeing his home. His head was so full of thoughts of how much his family home had changed that he wouldn't notice if a Messerschmitt flew nose to nose with the Mosquito. If Jiří agreed, they could be there in a couple of hours. He resisted the temptation to try and persuade Jiří, knowing his friend would be more likely to agree if left to think things over for himself.

Unfortunately, that gave Milan time to brood over Jess. As far as he could see, her decision did at least relieve him of the agonising choice of where to make his home. If she didn't want him, there was no reason to remain in England once he was finally out of the RAF.

After a long silence, Jiří's voice crackled over the intercom. 'Final target in five minutes.' Then, after a pause, 'What will the CO do when he finds out?'

'Who says he will?'

'We'll be hours late returning to Benson. How do we explain it?'

'We tell him we had engine trouble, had to make a forced landing to fix it. He need never know the truth.'

Another pause. Then, 'Very well. I'm in. On one condition – we look for my family first.'

Milan's stomach was in knots as he photographed the area around Dresden – the last known position of the 4th Panzer Army. In any other circumstances he would have been eager to look for signs of their retreat and surrender to the Red Army; now he strained his eyes to look south east, across the Czech frontier. That was where his home lay.

Jiří continued to give bearings, although Milan didn't need them now. Memories of training flights from his time in the Czechoslovak Air Force guided his way. Far below the silvery Elbe pointed him towards Prague until it doubled back on itself, then a little further on Milan caught his first glimpse of the Vltava for six years. He was losing height now, and he could make out individual fields, roads and clusters of buildings. Somewhere down there were his sister and nephew. He desperately prayed they were, at any rate. His longing for home was now so intense it was a physical pain gnawing at his stomach.

Jiří's voice crackled across the intercom. 'Where are we landing – Kbely?' This was the military airfield on the outskirts of Prague where they had been based in their Czechoslovak Air Force days.

Milan shook his head. 'We don't know if the Luftwaffe are still there. If they are, I don't fancy landing a British plane in the middle of them. The same goes for Ruzyně.'

'But there's nowhere else anywhere near Prague.'

'I know a place.' He banked, continuing to lose height. 'I got lost on my first solo cross-country flight. Didn't quite have enough fuel to make it to Kbely and had to make a forced landing in a field.'

'You're going to put us down in a field? Are you crazy?' Jiří's voice was sliding up the scale again.

'I did it before.'

'That was in a B-534. The Mosquito is twice the size.'

There was no denying Jiří had a point. An unseen obstacle such as a burrow or patch of soft ground could be enough to cause a crash. When Milan had landed in the field seven years ago, the short grass had concealed no obstacles and the ground was as hard as concrete. If nothing had changed, it would be safe to land there. However, seven years was a long time.

He glanced back at Jiří, eyebrows raised. 'If you've changed your mind, just say the word. I'll turn back.'

Jiří shook his head. 'I've not come this far only to return without finding my family.'

Milan turned his attention to the ground. Far below he could see the landing strip at Kbely and, further east, the line of trees that marked the edge of the field he was looking for. Holding his breath, he swooped low over the field, craning his neck to examine the ground. It looked just the same as it had the last time he had landed there with no visible obstructions.

'This is your last chance to back out.'

'No way.' Jiří's voice was strained but definite.

Milan circled the field, doing his best to judge wind direction then, every muscle in his body rigid with tension, glided down to land. The wheels hit firm ground, and the Mosquito bounced once then settled on the field.

Jiří swore as it rumbled over the rough surface and came to a controlled stop not far from the trees. 'Promise you'll never put me through anything like that again.'

Only when the propellers had swished to a stop did Milan shrug off his parachute and Mae West with trembling hands and undo his harness. He swivelled round and grinned at Jiří. 'Admit it, you enjoyed it.'

Jiří was still swearing as they climbed out onto the wing and jumped down to the ground. The first time Milan's feet had touched Czech soil for six years. He was tempted to kneel down and plunge his hands into the earth, but there was no time for melodramatic gestures. They had two families to find, and Milan wanted to get back to

Britain before dark. While the Mosquito was equipped for night flying, he didn't want to risk a night flight unless he absolutely had to.

'How do we get from here to Prague?' Jiří asked.

Milan opened his mouth then bit off his answer at the sound of shouts and running feet. Five men burst through the trees, armed with pitchforks and other dangerous looking farm equipment.

'Hands up,' cried one, first in Czech then in halting English. 'Who are you?'

Milan raised his hands in the air, and Jiří did likewise. 'Friends,' he called in Czech.

The men approached, their makeshift weapons raised. 'Prove it,' another called.

Milan gave a helpless shrug. 'How? We are both Czechs who have been flying with the British during the war.' He hesitated a moment then pulled his Foreign Air Personnel identity card from his breast pocket. It proclaimed that he was serving in the Czechoslovak Air Force and listed his ranks held in the RAF. He handed it to the man who seemed to be the leader, a tall, fair haired man in his forties or early fifties. Jiří did the same.

The man examined the cards, paying particular attention to the Air Ministry stamp. Finally he handed them back. 'They look genuine,' he said to the other men, who lowered their weapons. The man turned back to Milan and Jiří. 'Where are you from?'

'Vyšehrad,' Jiří said.

The leader jerked his head at Milan. 'And you?'

'Roztoky.'

'Why have the RAF sent you here?'

'If it's to aid the uprising, they're too late,' a scowling dark haired man said. 'The Red Army are here now. They saved us from the Nazis when the British and Americans left us to be shot like dogs.' Another man clasped him on the shoulder, and the dark haired man subsided.

Milan had a feeling he was missing something but didn't want to get involved in these men's problems. He could guess it was to do with the Americans withdrawing from Czechoslovakia after liberating Pilsen instead of pushing forwards into Prague, leaving the liberation of Czechoslovakia to the Russians. Much as he thought that decision was a terrible mistake, especially following the accidental bombing in February, it wasn't a discussion he was prepared to get into with strangers. 'The RAF didn't send us. We were on a mission to Dresden but took a little detour.'

This statement earned grins and nods of approval.

'Then why are you here?' the leader asked.

'To get news of our families. We haven't seen or heard from them in years. When Jiří here heard Vyšehrad had been bombed, I promised to come with him to Prague at the earliest opportunity.'

'You can't go around Prague in your uniforms.'

'Why not?'

'It's not safe. There are still members of the SS holed up and Nazi sympathisers. If you bump into the wrong crowd you could end up being lynched.'

Milan glanced at Jiří, his heart sinking. Coming here had been an impulse. He'd assumed that with the end of the war, all hostilities would be over. 'We have to go. We haven't come all this way just to fly home.'

The leader scratched his chin. 'I was going to visit my aunt in Prague tomorrow. I could go today instead and give you a lift. I'll find a couple of raincoats you can wear to cover up your uniforms. You must take care, though.

It is not only Nazi sympathisers you must avoid. There are plenty of people who do not forget that the British abandoned Czechoslovakia at the start of the war, and the British and Americans refused to help us fight the Nazis at the end, even when we appealed for help. Many people believe our future lies with Russia. Czechoslovakia is not safe for men who joined the British.'

Jiří scowled. 'Even though we fought the Nazis?'

The man looked sad. 'No one saw you fight. All the people here know is that we were left without help when the Nazis stormed our villages and shot men, women and children.'

–

The man dropped them near to the central train station, telling them he would drive out to Roztoky and meet them in the town centre at three if they wanted a ride back to the field. Before leaving, he pressed a few Bohemian koruny into Milan's hand. 'I'm not so poor I can't afford it,' he said when Milan tried to hand the money back.

Seeing Czech names on shops and street signs, and hearing Czech spoken all around them, Milan felt as though he had awoken from a long and feverish dream. It was surreal to walk onto the streets and find everything looked pretty much as he remembered. Having seen the devastation of the Blitz in London, Milan had feared he would see similar destruction in Prague. Now, however, he realised the Nazis had no reason to bomb a city they had been allowed to walk into with no resistance. He glanced at Jiří, who gazed around him looking like a sleeper who had been startled awake.

Suddenly overcome with a desire to see the Vltava, along whose banks he had strolled so many times, he said,

'Let's walk to the river. We can pick up a tram from there.' If anywhere could convince him he was finally home, it would be a sight of the river.

Jiří nodded, still looking dazed. They walked along Mezibranská and then turned right down Žitná. Without needing to say a word to each other, they both picked up their pace now they were heading directly for the river.

They were approaching Karlovo náměstí when Jiří gave a sharp intake of breath. 'The church. Look.' He pointed to where the church of St Ignatius stood. Or, rather, where it had stood.

Milan froze. A large section of the roof and walls had gone, exposing the interior. A pile of rubble was now all that remained of the outer stonework; snapped and charred beams lay scattered like discarded matchsticks. Further up the square, he could see the hospital had also been hit. The area around Karlovo náměstí was clearly one of the casualties of the tragic mistaken bombing on St Valentine's Day. This was a sight he was all too familiar with.

Unbidden, images of Jess's house flashed into his mind. Of picking his way through rubble in search of Hannah and Vera. Of holding Jess in his arms as she had sobbed in relief and poured out the truth about her past. At the time he had hoped that moment would mark a deepening of their relationship. He swallowed and rubbed his eyes as though it could erase the painful memory.

'This is awful,' Jiří said, white-faced. 'Worse than the London bombings somehow.'

Milan knew what he meant. Perhaps if they had known London before the war, he would have felt the same shock Jess had always displayed when they had passed a crater where once a place known to Jess had stood. He had been sickened by the loss of life, of course, but he couldn't feel the sorrow Jess felt at the damage to a much-loved city. Now, however, he guessed she must have felt the same sense of deep loss and wrongness he felt at seeing rubble instead of the beautiful Baroque church.

He cleared his throat. 'Come on. Let's see if the trams are still running.' Now, more than ever, he needed to find what had happened to his sister. He toyed with the idea of leaving Jiří while he went to Roztoky alone. Another glance at Jiří's face changed his mind. His friend was shaking, as though he had been struck by all the horrors of the war at once. He could not leave him to face what could be the loss of his whole family alone.

There was more shock to come when they reached the river and the wide road that ran parallel to its banks. The building that stood on the corner, facing the river, was now roofless and its interior a burnt-out shell.

He turned away from it and gazed across the river. With his back to the wreckage he could almost believe Prague had escaped the war unscathed. The water sparkled in the sunshine; the trees lining the banks whispered in the gentle breeze. On the far side, the wooded slopes of Petřín Hill rose up just as they had always done. The buildings that lined the banks on the west side looked largely untouched. Hearing the chug of boats, the hum of the crowds and the rattle of trams, he could almost believe the intervening years had been a dream and he was still an earnest music student with a glittering career ahead of him. Almost.

Jiří tugged his arm and pointed to a tram that had just pulled up at a stop. 'That's going the right way,' he said.

They jumped on board, and the tram moved off, ringing its bell as it followed the river south. When they passed the Palacký Bridge, Milan could see that, too, had been damaged. A sick knot of fear twisted in his stomach as the ramparts of Vyšehrad came into view. What would they find up there? The twin spires of the St Peter and Paul church were still thankfully intact. After seeing the damage to St Ignatius church, it was a relief to know that the church dominating the skyline in this part of Prague had survived.

They left the tram at the foot of the ramparts; Jiří led them up a narrow cobbled lane that climbed steeply up to meet the huddle of streets behind the historic fortifications.

'How far to your house?' Milan clutched a stitch in his side. After so long in the Mosquito, his muscles were protesting at the exercise.

'Not far. It is just around—' Jiří stopped short with a choking cry. The reason was all too clear. The street beyond had been reduced to rubble.

Milan, seeing Jiří swaying in shock, grabbed him by the arm. 'It might not be as bad as it looks,' he said. 'They might not have been in the house. Where else could they be?' This was all too horribly like seeing Jess's home destroyed.

At first, Jiří gave no sign that he had heard. He continued to stare at the ruins. 'Our apartment was just there.' He pointed to the middle of the rubble.

Milan gripped Jiří's arm harder. 'Think. Where would they have gone?'

Jiří seemed to emerge from his daze. 'My aunt's house, perhaps.'

'Where is she?' Milan could see they would not be going to Roztoky any time soon but he couldn't leave Jiří in this state.

'Not far.' Jiří pointed vaguely back towards the ramparts.

Milan's hopes rose. The area around the ancient fortifications had appeared relatively unscathed. 'If they were there they might have escaped,' he said. 'Your aunt at least will be able to tell you what has happened.'

Jiří nodded and led the way. They didn't speak at all throughout the ten-minute walk through narrow, winding streets. Jiří's face was strained; Milan could only guess what he must be going through. If his thoughts were anything like Milan's, he would be dwelling on the wreckage that had once been his home and praying his family had escaped.

Jiří broke the silence when they turned onto a cobbled lane that sloped steeply down towards the river. It was not far from the road they had climbed from the tram. 'Teta Lenka's house is down there,' he said.

He blew out a shaky breath and descended the hill. The houses here were old, not the tenement blocks that lined the main streets but low houses only one or two storeys high, all painted white and roofed with terracotta tiles. The similarity to Milan's home made his throat tighten.

They rounded a bend and Milan saw a tiny woman sweeping the front step of a small two-storeyed house. She paused a moment, putting a hand to her back and glanced up at the approaching men. Milan wouldn't have thought anything of it if Jiří hadn't stopped dead. '*Maminko?*'

His voice came as little more than a whisper, but the woman reacted as though she had been shot. She pressed a hand to her chest. '*Jiříku.*' Her lips were trembling. 'It can't be.'

Then she flung the broom aside and ran up the street towards them. Jiří dashed to meet her. Jiří's mother pulled Jiří into her arms and wept. Although her head didn't reach any higher than her son's chest, she still managed to give the impression of a mother hen fussing over one of her chicks. Milan stayed where he was, not wanting to intrude on this private moment. He stepped back a little so as not to overhear.

Finally Jiří murmured something and pointed at Milan. Taking that as his signal, he approached.

'*Maminko*, this is my friend, Milan.'

'Come in, come in,' Mrs Stepanek cried. 'Any friend of my son's is welcome here. We are cooking lunch.'

Milan hesitated, aware that time was short. 'I must find my own family.'

After a quick discussion, they decided that Milan would take the train to Roztoky, and Jiří would get a lift from a neighbour and meet him there.

As Milan was about to leave, Jiří pulled him into a hug. His eyes glistened with tears, and his haunted expression had eased for the first time since hearing of the Prague bombing. 'I can't thank you enough for bringing me to Prague.' Then he grinned, displaying the humour that had been sadly missing these past few months. 'But if the CO works out where we've been, I'm telling him you flew me here against my will.'

Milan clapped him on the shoulder. 'Careful, or I might fly back without you. I'll tell the CO you annoyed me so much, I threw you out of the plane. He'd definitely understand.'

Laughing, he set out for the tram and train journey to Roztoky. However, all laughter died when he reached Masarykovo train station and he saw the stonework pocked with what could only be bullet holes. Milan turned away from the sight, overcome with fresh fears for Eliška and Franta. He was finally going home, but would they be there?

Chapter Twenty-Six

Slogging up the hill from Roztoky railway station, Milan felt disoriented. This was the journey he repeated night after night in his dreams yet now he was wide awake. He could only pray the end of this walk would have the same outcome. The knot in his stomach tightened as he turned up yet another steep cobbled street. Everything looked just as it had the last time he had seen it.

The May sunshine warmed his face as he walked, and the scent of sun-warmed pine floated on the air. His sense of unreality increased as the road led into the woods and he gazed up at the fresh green of new leaves waving against the clear blue sky. Every now and then Milan would catch a glimpse of russet as a squirrel darted along a branch, and birdsong trilled, punctuated every now and again by the resonant tapping of a woodpecker.

Then, around the bend of the track, Milan saw the wooden gate. This was it. Home.

He put his hand to the gate's catch then stopped. In his dream he would always see his sister and Franta, but this was where the likeness to the dream ended. Eliška wasn't there, and instead of Franta, a boy of about nine or ten years of age was crouched in the vegetable patch pulling out weeds.

Milan's heart gave a lurch. Eliška must have moved away, but who was this living in the home his family had lived in for generations? A wave of despair swept over him. He must have made a sound, for the boy looked up. He sprang to his feet with a wary look on his face when he saw a stranger. He looked towards the house. '*Maminko!*' he called and ran inside, slamming the door behind him.

Milan stood, unmoving, a leaden weight crushing his chest. If Eliška wasn't here, he had no idea where to look. He had lost Jess, and now it looked like he had lost his family.

Finally deciding that the people living here now might know what had happened, he drew a deep breath, pushed open the gate and stepped into the yard.

Then the door flew open, and a young woman appeared. Her hair was dark, almost black. The same colour as Milan's. Her face had the same high cheekbones as his mother. Although he could not see the colour of her eyes, he knew they would be a piercing blue.

His throat seemed to seize up. He tried to call her name but no words would come out. He walked up the path.

'Milan, is that really you?' Her voice was unchanged, the familiar tones finally shaking Milan from his despair.

'Eliška. I thought…'

The boy he had seen before came outside again. Now he held a hockey stick, his expression so fierce Milan had to bite back a laugh.

Milan glanced between him and Eliška. 'This is Franta?' He shook his head. 'I am an idiot. All these years I've thought of you as a baby. I forgot you would have grown up. And old enough to look after your mother now.'

The boy frowned. 'How do you know me?' He raised the stick. 'Stay back. I am not afraid to use this.'

'Franta, put that down. This is your uncle. I told you he would come back one day.'

Franta lowered the stick although he did not put it down.

Milan took a step closer. 'You won't remember me, but I remember you.' He cleared his throat, struggling to repress a sob. The tiny child he had cuddled and vowed to protect was gone, replaced by this fierce wildcat. A wave of desolation swept over him as it hit him just what he had lost.

Eliška ran the rest of the way down the path and flung herself into Milan's arms. Then they were both crying.

'I knew you were safe,' Eliška said when she could speak again. She dabbed away her tears with the sleeve of her blouse. 'Everyone told me you were probably dead, but I knew I would feel it if you had died. Come in. We have so much to talk about.'

They had so little time, not nearly enough to share all that had happened in their six years apart. Soon he would need to meet Jiří and return to RAF Benson. For now, though, it was enough to know that his family was safe. Milan could see out his remaining time in England secure in the knowledge that Eliška and Franta would be waiting when he returned. Hopefully now the disorienting dreams would stop.

–

While the war in Europe had been raging, Jess had been able to take satisfaction in her work and know she was making a valuable contribution. Now, although the skies were still busy with flights going back and forth, Jess found it harder to keep her mind on her work. Again and again her thoughts would stray to Milan. She had the feeling she was standing on the brink of a precipice, and when she fully accepted she would never see him again, she would plunge over the edge and never stop falling.

Nevertheless, she had been right to end things when she had. Despite his protestations, she knew he could never feel the same way about her now he knew about Hannah. If he had truly loved her, he would have given some sign he saw a future with her. It was far better to make a clean break now and leave him free to return to Czechoslovakia. Far better than wait for weeks or months in hope before he wrote explaining he had met someone else. A good Czechoslovakian girl who did not have a ruined reputation.

A pity knowing she was right did nothing to numb the pain.

At least the scaling down of work gave her more time to spend with Evie and May, although all the talk of wedding plans was like rubbing sand into a bleeding wound. Still, she bathed her eyes every morning so they would never guess how many silent tears she shed every night; she even managed to summon a display of enthusiasm over discussions about rings and dresses, not wanting to spoil her friends' happiness. And when May spoke glumly of having no family around her for her wedding, Jess did her best to cheer her up.

'I've had a wonderful idea,' Evie said to May one evening after returning from a date with Alex. 'I've talked it over with Alex and he agrees. How would you and Peter like to make it a double wedding at Amberton? There's still time to make the necessary arrangements.'

May had been studying her engagement ring, twisting it around her finger. Now her eyes suddenly seemed to come to life, as though the sparkling diamonds in her ring reflected in their depths. 'Truly? Are you sure? That would be marvellous. I can't think of anywhere I'd rather get married, and to celebrate with you would be the icing on the cake.'

The two girls hugged. 'I mean,' May hastened to add, 'I'll have to discuss it with Peter, of course, but I'm sure he'll be as thrilled as I am. Amberton's not far from Portsmouth so it will be easy for his parents to get there.'

From there the conversation turned to flowers (wild flowers picked from the hedgerows), reception (sandwiches at the local pub) and bridesmaids (Jess for Evie and Peggy for May). Peggy, the evacuee girl May and Jess had befriended in Amberton, was still living at the vicarage there. The moment May thought of her, she ripped a page from one of Evie's exercise books and insisted upon writing to ask straight away.

Jess joined in with the discussions with enthusiasm but couldn't help a sigh of relief when another officer, who had gone to answer the ringing phone, held the receiver towards Jess. 'Phone for you, Jess.'

'Jess, so glad I caught you.' The smooth tones of Leo came through loud and clear. 'I'm doing an interview with a reporter who's doing a piece on the film. He's anxious to meet you. Keen on the romance angle, you know.'

Jess glanced across at Evie and May, still wrapped up in their wedding plans. 'I'll be free in the afternoon,' she said.

–

'So, Miss Halloway… or may I call you Jess?' The reporter, a portly man with a sweaty red face leaned across the table towards her, breathing whisky fumes in her face. Whether by accident or design, his leg brushed against hers under the table.

Jess leaned back in her seat and crossed her legs, catching him a sharp blow on the ankle. 'Oops. So sorry.' She tapped the bands on her sleeve. 'And it's Section Officer Halloway, actually.'

Only five minutes into the interview and she bitterly regretted agreeing to it. She should have known what it would be like when the reporter had insisted upon meeting her in a pub. Jess, who was on duty that night, had asked the reporter to meet her in Stanmore. That meant that she was being interviewed alone, without the support of any other cast members. She wished she'd asked Evie and May to come along to keep an eye on her from another table. Now more than ever she was remembering the sleazy side of show business. During the grim years of the war her memories of the glitz and glamour had provided a welcome antidote to wartime austerity. How could she have forgotten being pawed by directors who insisted they could help her hit the big time if only she co-operated?

Of course, that was what Leo had done, too, only his debonair persona made it harder to see his true motives. When she had been a young, naive actress struggling to make a name for herself, she had been flattered by his attention and allowed him to fool her into thinking he was doing her a favour. In fact he had just used her and now was trying to use her again. She had known it all along, really.

What was it Evie had said? Something about punishing herself. She hadn't really understood at the time but now it all fell into place. Ever since Leo had reappeared in her life, she had been unable to understand why he had such a hold on her, why she seemed to be drawn to his company. Every time she'd agreed to go out with Leo, she'd made excuses for his behaviour, telling herself it was necessary for her career. Whereas the truth was that deep down, she believed she didn't deserve better. She hadn't felt worthy of Milan's love.

Milan! What had she done? The bravest, most steadfast, not to mention good looking man in the world had made it clear he loved her, and she had pushed him away. No wonder Evie and May had become so exasperated with her.

'Tell me, Jess,' the reporter said, cutting through her thoughts, 'How did you feel when you were asked to take a role in the film?'

Jess, too dazed from her revelation, missed her chance to take him to task for calling her Jess again. By the time she drew breath to object, the reporter had ploughed on. 'You must have been so excited when you heard you were to play opposite Leonard Steele. Yes, I can see the headlines now. Humble WAAF rescued from office job by heroic RAF film star. Have you set a date for the wedding yet?'

Jess could have borne just about any insult, but to hear six years of vital work dismissed as an office job, in the same breath as having Leo branded a hero simply because he wore RAF uniform, was too much. The worst of it was, she couldn't correct the patronising git because she had signed the Official Secrets Act.

That was it. She had had enough. 'No. We won't be setting a date,' she said. 'The wedding is off. I made a terrible mistake and I'm undoing it before it's too late.'

The reporter's pen hovered over his notebook. 'Tell me more.' Jess had the impression he would have liked to rub his hands.

Jess didn't care. She was through with pretence. 'There isn't much more to tell. I'm in love with another man.' There, she had said it. It felt good to have the truth out in the open. She only wished she could be saying it to Milan instead of this vulture of a reporter.

'This other man. Who is he?'

She sat up straight, feeling the weight lift from her shoulders. 'That's my business. Nothing will come of it. I know 'e doesn't love me. That's no reason to marry the wrong man, though.' She couldn't feel bad about Leo finding out this way. He had not only used her, he had announced their so-called engagement publicly in a way that had made it impossible for her to deny it. And in front of Milan, too. Well, he was reaping his reward now.

The reporter was scribbling notes so fast Jess thought the paper might catch fire. 'What did Leonard Steele say when you told him?'

It was on the tip of her tongue to say Leo knew nothing of it. However, she bit it back. Let Leo choose to make of this what he would. He had forced Jess's hand, and perhaps if she had thought things through, she wouldn't have blurted all this to a reporter of all people. It was done now, however. She couldn't regret it. She also wouldn't reveal what Leo was really like because she couldn't find it in her heart to wish him ill. He had been selfish and thoughtless but not malicious. She could forgive him. 'That's between me and him,' she said.

The man frowned as he read his notes through. 'Rumour has it there's a Hollywood studio interested in the pair of you. Chances are, they'll drop you like a ton of bricks when they see this.'

'It doesn't matter.' Jess drained her lemonade and rose. Her brain must be working properly for the first time in months, because now it was obvious who she was and what she wanted to do with her life. 'I'm a WAAF, and I'll stay with 'em for as long as they'll 'ave me.'

She strode out of the pub feeling as light as air. She knew what she was going to do.

As luck would have it, the first person she saw when she walked into the anteroom at Bentley Manor was her CO.

'I was planning on talking to everyone about the future,' Laura Morgan said when Jess approached her. 'Now seems as good a time as any. When the demob process begins, it's going to be chaos. However, as you volunteered fairly early in the war, you shouldn't have too long a wait. The WAAF are adopting a first in, first out policy.'

'Oh. But I was hoping I could stay.'

'Stay? I thought you were going to be an actress.'

'I thought I was but I realised my heart wasn't in it. I didn't fully realise how important the WAAF was to me until recently. I do now, though, and want to stay as long as possible. Make a career of it, I mean.'

Laura gave Jess a broad smile. 'I can't tell you how pleased I am to hear it. Of course, work in the Filter Room will be winding down. However, there is a role I think you're ideally suited to.'

Jess sat up. Her CO had actually considered her for a future role? She had always thought they wouldn't make any effort to retain her after the war. 'What's that?'

'I've long thought you would make an excellent teacher. I've watched you with your friends and your juniors, and I've admired the way you encourage them. Bring out their best. We want to make the WAAF into a good career for women, and we're going to need the best instructors. You've taken on varied roles during the war, so you would be ideally suited.'

'Thank you. That sounds wonderful.'

'How did the interview go?' Evie asked a little later when Jess met up with her and May as they prepared to head to the Filter Room for their next watch.

'I'll tell you on the way,' Jess said. 'I have to phone Leo first.' She had no doubt the reporter would be contacting Leo for his reaction to her interview, and, much as she thought he deserved finding out with no warning, she decided to be the better person and warn him.

—

'Imagine me, an instructor officer,' Jess said to Evie and May as they strolled out of the Filter Room the next morning. As Laura Morgan had said, work in the Filter Room was winding down. All the old urgency was gone now there was no danger of enemy aircraft or V2s attacking Britain. The focus of the RAF had shifted to the war in the east, which still raged, and relief work in Europe, neither of which offered much work for the WAAFs of Bentley Priory. Jess knew that some WAAFs were now working in Europe. She had heard of some who could speak other languages being used to guide visiting officials around places the Nazis had used as prisons. One WAAF had returned from a brief tour looking distinctly shaken and had refused to say what she had seen.

'I think you'll be perfect for the role,' Evie told her. 'I don't know why I didn't think of it before, but you're the one who showed me the ropes in my early days.'

'Yes, and you were a brilliant teacher when I was learning to act,' May said, speaking of the time Jess had offered to give her acting lessons to improve her confidence.

'Jess Halloway, instructor officer,' Jess said, grinning. 'Who'd have thought it?'

'Are you sure you won't regret giving up acting, though?' May asked. 'I thought you loved it.'

'I do. But you know, the acting role I most loved was playing Cinderella in the panto at Amberton. I couldn't work out what was different, but after the CO said her piece, it all fell into place.' She paused, enjoying again the feeling of hearing Laura Morgan's praise. 'I did enjoy the acting, no doubt about that, but what I enjoyed most was the organisation, seeing it all come together, knowing it was because of me that it was all happening. And, best of all, seeing you bloom, May, and produce an amazing performance.' Jess paused. 'Anyway, acting's clearly not good for me. I was so blinded by the possibility of fame, I couldn't see where my true talents lie. And maybe...' She swallowed. She had been about to wonder aloud if she should have spent more time with Milan rather than persuading herself she needed to mix with other actors for the sake of her career. But it was still too painful to speak his name.

'So you're saying goodbye to a film career.' Thankfully, May didn't appear to have noticed Jess's hesitation.

'Yup. Well, not completely, of course. I've still got the première to get through. Then I'll be saying goodbye. You are coming, aren't you? I know you're busy with the wedding preparations, but I couldn't bear to go through it without the two of you.' It should have been an exciting occasion with Milan on her arm. Now she was dreading it, especially after her interview went public.

'Course we'll come,' Evie said. 'Try and stop us.'

'I'm really looking forward to it,' May said. 'It will be my first and probably only glimpse of a showbiz life.'

'Trust me, it's overrated,' Jess said. 'Talking of the showbiz life, though, that reminds me. I need to get a paper. That interview will be out. I bet Leo's wishing he hadn't pushed me into it now.'

They had left Hill House by this time, so Jess went down the hill towards the shops and found a newspaper boy on the corner of the Uxbridge Road. Then she hurried back up the hill to Bentley Manor, the paper rolled under her arm.

'I've got to admit, I haven't felt this nervous since we were tracking a V2 heading right for Bentley Priory,' Jess said once she'd joined her friends in the anteroom and opened the paper.

She didn't have to search too hard. On page four, the headline stood out: 'Actress Jilts Steele.' Jess winced. 'Here we go,' she muttered, and read the article.

> When actor Leonard Steele announced his engagement to the unknown Jessica Halloway a little over two weeks ago, the British were full of good wishes for the happy couple and ready to welcome Halloway into their hearts. Little did he know that the small-time actress turned WAAF would turn around to bite him only a few days later.
>
> 'I made a terrible mistake,' says Halloway, 24. 'I am in love with another man.' When

she realised this man didn't love her in return, she claims she allowed Leonard Steele to sweep her off her feet. She now claims she can't go through with the wedding and has decided to focus on her career.

It's only to be hoped that Leonard Steele chooses more wisely next time. When approached for his reaction to Halloway's desertion, he said, 'I wish her all the best in the future. My heart is broken but it wasn't meant to be.'

Jess tossed the paper aside with an exclamation of disgust. 'He's changed his tune since I spoke to him.'

'Why? What did he say?' Evie asked.

'Told me I could forget ever landing another acting job, that he would see me finished. Like I care.'

'What a...' Evie seemed to grope for words. In the end she grabbed the paper, screwed it into a tight ball and flung it into the waste paper basket.

'Are you sure you still want to go to the première?' May asked.

'I'm going with my 'ead 'eld 'igh.' Jess pointed to the crumpled paper in the bin. 'I'll show the readers of that rag that I've done nothing to be ashamed of. Besides—' she grinned at her friends '—this is my last chance for a showbiz party and I'm not going to let Leo spoil it.'

The rumble of an aero engine made her glance through the open window; a Spitfire was gliding through the blue sky. She watched it, her thoughts flying to Milan, and her defiant mood faded. Where was he? Would she ever see him again? She doubted it. Idiot that she was, she had pushed him away not once but twice. Even if he did still love her, he wouldn't risk getting hurt a third time.

Chapter Twenty-Seven

The dream came again that night. He was returning home after years away, walking down the track beside the woods, watching eagerly for the bend in the road and the first glimpse of his family home. Then he saw it – the terracotta tiles glowing a brilliant orange in contrast to the green woodland beyond. Franta was running down the road to meet him, Eliška only a few steps behind.

'Uncle Milan!' Franta cried. 'It's Uncle Milan.'

Then Milan reached them. He flung his bag to the ground and hoisted Franta into the air, swinging him around. All he could see was Franta's smiling face against the blur of green branches and blue sky. Finally he put Franta down and staggered dizzily to Eliška. 'It is so good to be home,' he said.

The shrill ringing of his alarm clock woke him, and he fumbled an arm from his tangled blankets and turned it off. He lay on his back, staring at the ceiling while his sleep-fogged brain grappled with where he was. Then it all came back to him. He was in his quarters at RAF Benson, having returned from Prague without his CO suspecting what he and Jiří had done. All was well. So why had he dreamed about home again? He'd thought those dreams would end now he had been back and seen for himself that Eliška and Franta were safe.

Something was hammering in the far recesses of his brain, trying to catch his attention, telling him something had been different about the dream. Several times he thought he almost had it; each time, the elusive difference slipped from his consciousness before he could capture it. The more he thought about it, the further it sank from his grasp.

After a while he gave a groan and pulled himself into a sitting position. He put his hands to his face and found to his surprise that his cheeks were wet with tears. What was wrong with him? He had been home, found everyone safe. Yes, Prague had suffered but it could be rebuilt. So why had a dream that should have been happy made him so sad? Even Franta, who in real life had needed time to get used to him, had ran up to him and called him Uncle.

Uncle. Franta had called him Uncle. In English. That was when it hit him like a bullet to the chest. He had dreamt of home, yet every word had been spoken in English. As far as he could remember, he had always dreamed in Czech, even when his dreams had been about England. It had been one of his few links to home. Yet even though this had been a clear dream of reunion with his family, every word had been in English.

Perhaps it hadn't been a dream of homecoming after all. Perhaps it was his subconscious finally letting go of the past, saying goodbye.

–

Milan still felt shaky when it was time for breakfast, too churned up to eat. As the squadron were currently being rested and had no flying duties that day, he decided to do the only thing that might settle his whirling thoughts. He skipped breakfast and took his violin to the distant hangar where he always practised. Opening up the violin case after his absence was like reacquainting himself with an old friend. The ritual of tightening the bow and applying rosin then tuning the strings helped calm him. He began with a series of scales and arpeggios and soon he had reached that point where his fingers seemed to move without conscious thought. It was as though there was a connection between the violin and his fingers that completely bypassed his brain. He could almost feel his shoulders lightening as his worries fell away. He wouldn't think about the dream any more. He would lose himself in music for an hour or so and come back to the problem later.

Feeling it was time to play some music, he put down the violin and searched in the pocket where he kept his sheet music. His fingers closed around a small piece of card. Pulling it out he saw the card that he vaguely remembered from the concert. He read the name. Douglas Murray. That sounded familiar. Where had he heard it before?

Wait. Douglas Murray the renowned composer? Douglas Murray the founder of the Murray Orchestra? Milan had heard of him. He supposed he hadn't made the connection earlier because he'd thought Murray was part of the film world. What had he said when he'd handed over his card? Milan racked his brains. It was hard to remember exactly because his head had been full of Leonard Steele's outrageous announcement at the time. Something about getting in touch if Milan planned to stay in the country.

The beginnings of hope formed. Murray could only have made the suggestion if he thought he could offer

Milan work. Maybe there would be something for Milan in Britain if he decided to stay. The question was, did he want to stay when Jess did not want him?

—

When Milan went into the mess that evening he picked up a discarded newspaper and sank onto a sofa to catch up with the news. He flicked through the headlines – they all dealt with world events which he had already heard about or experienced for himself. But when he saw the headline on page four, he gripped the paper, crumpling it in his fist. He skimmed the article, his heart hammering. Jess had publicly declared she was in love with another man. The line that tore through his heart was the fact that she had believed her love to be unreturned.

All his worries about his future faded to insignificance. If Jess loved him, he knew they could work something out. The only thing that mattered now was to find her and make her understand that he loved her.

He dashed to the phone, only to find a young pilot officer apparently deeply involved in a conversation with his girlfriend. It was all Milan could do not to wrench the receiver from his hand as he breathed endearments down the line. Especially as he had heard the same man have a very similar conversation the day before with a different girl.

After what felt like an age, the pilot officer hung up after many promises to love the unfortunate girl for ever. Milan snatched the receiver and put a call through to Bentley Manor. He had lost track of Jess's watches so could only pray she was off duty.

'Halloway?' said the woman who answered. She barked her words out so loudly Milan had to hold the receiver away from his ear. 'She'll be out all night. She's got that fancy première in Leicester Square tonight.'

'What time?'

'Eight, I think.'

Milan replaced the receiver and glanced at his watch. He might just make it. Seeing his CO walk into the anteroom, he marched up to him. 'Your car. I need it.'

'I say, you can't just—'

'It's important. Please.'

Squadron Leader Dacre must have picked up Milan's urgency for after a pause where he studied Milan with narrowed eyes, he finally gave a tiny shrug and handed him the keys. 'But if you put so much as a scratch on it, I'll—'

Milan was out of the door before he heard the end of the sentence.

–

Jess peered ahead as she, Evie and May emerged from Leicester Square underground station. 'Blimey, there are loads of people.' She felt a qualm to see the crowds lining the entrance to the cinema. When she had been younger, she had dreamed that one day she would be greeted by cheering crowds as she arrived at a première. Now, even though her dreams had come true, she couldn't help wishing no one had turned up. 'I bet they're Leo's fans. If they've read the papers, they won't be 'appy with me.' The report she had seen first hadn't been the only one. One particularly vitriolic report had called her 'Jilting Jess', and other papers had followed.

Evie squeezed her arm. 'Best foot forward, Jess. You're a star. Enjoy the moment.'

May, too, looked out. She turned pale. 'Isn't there a back door we can use?'

'I wish,' Jess muttered. She pulled her compact from her pocket to check her hair, but her hand shook so much she dropped it. She stooped to retrieve it, and when she looked up it was to see Leo leap out of a chauffeur-driven Rolls Royce to the cheers of the crowd.

Strangely, the sight gave her courage. She wouldn't let him get the better of her. 'Come on,' she said to Evie and May. 'Let's show 'em what true grit really means.'

At first, she had been disappointed that she would have to appear in uniform rather than a glamorous gown. Now she took strength in her uniform and the knowledge that she was part of something bigger than her. She shrank from walking out alone, though, and wished she could walk in between Evie and May. However, May would hate being the centre of attention, and she didn't think Evie would particularly enjoy it, so she let them slip unnoticed around the back of the crowd.

'Chin up, shoulders back, stand tall and sparkle,' she muttered to herself. She faltered momentarily, wishing Milan could be there with her. It was her fault he wasn't, though, so she pushed him out of her mind and strode out in front of the crowd.

Then a flash went off in her face, and she recovered, forcing a smile as bright as the lights festooning the cinema.

'Miss Halloway, Jess!'

Jess smiled and waved in the direction of the voice. Her heart gave a lurch when she saw a man holding a notebook and pencil. She supposed she should be grateful he hadn't called her Jilting Jess. She'd known there would be reporters there all aching to get a quote from her about

326

the end of her engagement to Leo, so she had prepared a few non-committal words. However, she hoped to get into the cinema without being stopped. Ahead of her she could see Evie and May had reached the safety of the door and were standing just inside. Leo was chatting to fans, smiling and waving and also answering questions fired to him by reporters.

Above the noise of the crowd, she heard one of them ask, 'How do you feel now you've been left in the lurch?'

Upset he couldn't use her to get a deal with the Hollywood studio, Jess wanted to retort. Still, she wanted to hear the answer, so she edged closer, covering the move by smiling at a teenage girl who was waving her autograph book at her. Jess gave her a beaming smile and scrawled her name on the page, all the while straining her ears to hear Leo's reply.

'I can't deny I'm heartbroken,' Leo said.

Jess made a supreme effort not to glare in Leo's direction. She could sense heads turning to look at her.

'But,' Leo went on, 'part of life is learning to deal with the ups as well as the downs. I won't let this beat me.'

Jess cast her gaze heavenwards. Leo certainly knew how to play an audience. Then she saw Leo glance her way and affect a start. His brilliant smile faltered and when he smiled again, there was the merest hint of pain in his eyes. If that little performance didn't win him an Oscar, the judges should have their heads examined.

'Excuse me,' Leo said. 'I—' his voice caught; he turned sharply, making for the doorway, one hand shielding his face from view. The crowd watched him go amid a murmur of concern.

'Miss Halloway.' The reporter who had tried to get her attention before called to her again. As though sensing blood, the crowd turned to her as one. Jess braced herself. Leo had made sure that she would suffer. 'Did you deliberately set out to break the heart of one of our best-loved actors?'

'She's shot herself in the foot,' called out someone from the crowd. 'No one else'll 'ave her now she's revealed her true colours.'

Jess wanted to do nothing more than copy Leo and flee for the shelter of the cinema. She cast a longing glance towards the door and took strength from the concerned faces of Evie and May. Whatever happened, she would always have their friendship. Leo, for all his adoring fans, would never know friendship like theirs. Leo, too, stood just inside, talking to the director. Jess couldn't decide who she'd rather face, the crowd or Leo.

She drew a deep breath, racking her brains for the right words. Nothing she had planned would satisfy the mob, so she decided to cast caution to the winds and speak from the heart.

'I'm truly sorry for any hurt I've caused.' None, in Leo's case, so she had no qualms about saying it. 'However, staying in a relationship when my heart was given elsewhere would have caused far greater pain. I hope Leonard will come to understand and forgive.' Forgive her for costing him a lucrative deal? Not likely.

'Jess!'

Heaven help her. Not another one. Why wouldn't they let her be? She turned up the beam on her smile a little brighter and looked for the speaker. And froze.

The man leaning across the barrier, waving to catch her attention, was Milan.

Chapter Twenty-Eight

For a horrible moment Jess thought her knees would give way. The noise of the crowd faded away, and her vision tunnelled until she could see nothing but Milan's face, his brows drawn together, his gaze meeting hers with an intensity that seemed to pierce her to the soul. She had to be dreaming. The stresses of the war had finally caught up with her.

Then her hearing cleared, and the scene came back into focus. She wasn't hallucinating; Milan was still there, reaching out towards her.

'Milan. What are you doing here?' She was intensely aware that she and Milan were now the centre of attention, and every word they said was being written down. She didn't care. All she cared was that Milan was there. She had one last chance to mend matters with him.

A reporter called out. 'Is this the man you're in love with.'

She didn't hesitate. 'Yes.'

A sigh rippled around the crowd. Jess could see smiling faces, handkerchiefs dabbing at eyes. However, the only person whose reaction she cared one jot about was Milan. She looked him straight in the eyes as she said, 'My heart was always his. I just didn't realise until it was too late. Or I thought it was too late.'

Like spectators at a tennis match, heads swivelled to face Milan.

Milan didn't tear his gaze from hers for an instant. 'It is not too late,' he said.

Jess thought her heart would burst, she didn't think it was possible for it to contain such joy. There was no need now to force a smile. She didn't think she would ever stop smiling.

'I came to apologise,' he said.

'You don't have to—'

'Yes I do.'

Seeing there was no stopping him, she held her tongue. The crowd were definitely going to get more than they'd bargained for this evening.

'This past year I have been torn,' he said. 'Torn between my duty to my family and my country and my love for you.'

Love. He still loved her. Her lips began to quiver; she pressed them together, determined not to embarrass herself by bursting into tears in front of their avid audience. It meant she couldn't speak.

'But I have been back to Czechoslovakia, and I have discovered that if I return there to live, my heart will never be whole because you would not be there. I will always love my country but I love you more. I did not say so before because I thought it was unfair to ask you to come with me to Czechoslovakia, and I thought I had nothing to offer you if I stayed in Britain.'

Jess approached the barrier. She spoke in a low voice, hoping no one could overhear. However, it was clear the observers were transfixed and holding their collective breath to catch every word. She gave a mental shrug and carried on. She would not leave until she had made it perfectly clear to Milan how much she loved him. 'All I want from you is you,' she said. 'I love you as you are. Whatever you decide to do with your life, it won't change my feelings for you.'

Milan gave a wry smile. 'You must allow me my male pride,' he said. 'I would be ashamed if I could not earn my way. But you are right. The most important thing is making sure you know how I feel. All the rest we can work out later.'

He dropped to one knee. There were gasps from the crowd and Jess swore she heard a sob. She could have cried herself, but she blinked back the tears. The vision of Milan swam before her. He was bathed with the lights from the cinema, lit with bright flashes as photographers lined up the shots that would appear in tomorrow's papers.

'Jessica Josephine Jane Halloway, will you do me the honour of being my wife?'

The crowd drew a breath as one. All heads turned to face her. From the corner of her eye she saw Evie and May jumping up and down in the foyer, clapping their hands.

'Yes, of course I will, you great numbskull.'

Applause and cheers split the air. So many flashes went off, Jess had her own private firework display seared onto her retinas.

Milan leapt over the barrier and swung Jess into his arms. If this was a film, now would be the perfect time to kiss her hero, so she did.

–

The church bells rang out as the west door was flung open and the two brides and their brand new grooms left the church in a hail of confetti. Jess, as maid of honour to both brides, was on the arm of the best man, who just happened to be Milan. She couldn't resist glancing at her hand as it rested on Milan's arm. As they walked out into the summer sunshine, the light caught in the trio of diamonds glinting from her new ring.

It was lovely to hear the bells pealing. After the church bells had been silenced for so long, she still thrilled every time she heard them.

She and Peggy, who had blossomed from a surly, unhappy eight-year-old to a pretty girl in her early teens since Jess had last seen her, helped Evie and May arrange their veils and bouquets for the photographs. Jess's face ached from smiling, she was so happy for her friends; Evie and May looked as though they felt the same way. After the long years of the war, when they had feared some or all of them wouldn't survive to see peace, they now had their reward.

'It feels strange to be back in Amberton, does it not?' Milan murmured to her as they stood back to allow Evie and Alex to stand on the church steps alone for their photograph.

'I know what you mean,' Jess said. 'I keep expecting Flight Officer Ellerby to leap out from behind a tree to put me on a charge for being out of uniform.' She couldn't resist a glance down at the pretty floral dress May and Evie had insisted upon clubbing together to have made for her. It would double up as her going away outfit when she and Milan married in August.

'It will always be a special place for me,' Milan said. 'It is where we met.'

'You always know the right thing to say to a girl,' Jess said. She stood on tiptoe and planted a kiss on his lips. Milan slid an arm around her waist before she could pull away and deepened the kiss. Finally she escaped and swatted his arm. 'Don't you be getting fresh with me, Milan Mašek.' But she shot him a smile that promised more kisses when they were out of the public eye.

'I think Amberton would be a lovely place to live.' Milan said. 'What do you say? When I am not on tour and you are not encouraging new WAAFs to be their best selves, how would you like to have a home in Amberton to come to? We could have a room for Hannah, of course.'

For Milan had spoken to Douglas Murray to find the eminent composer had been enthusiastic about Milan's potential as a concert violinist. Murray was working on a violin concerto, inspired by the performance Milan had given in Stanmore, and was keen for Milan to be the first to perform it. Of course, Milan was still in the RAF and was also applying for British citizenship, so was not yet free to perform, but it looked like all would go smoothly.

Jess looked around the village with a reminiscent smile, taking in the flint church, the pretty cottages and shops. 'You know, I always thought I was a London girl through and through, but something about this place really gets to me. I think we could be happy here. And it would be wonderful to be able to offer Jack, Vera and Hannah a place to stay whenever they want a break from the noise of London.'

They had talked it over with Vera and decided that it would soon be time to tell her that Jess was her real mother. Much as Jess longed to be a mother to Hannah, there was no question of tearing her away from the only mother she had known and loved. Vera and Jack couldn't have loved her any more had she been their true daughter, and it would have been cruel to separate them. Jess was determined to be the next best mother she could, however, and wanted Hannah to know she had two mothers who loved her with all their heart. Milan and Jess had decided to wait before trying for a family of their own, both wanting to make a good go of their careers first. Jess would be required to leave the WAAF if she became pregnant and wanted to leave on her terms after ensuring she had trained a good number of WAAFs to help with the work of rebuilding Europe.

At last the two happy couples had all the photographs they could wish for, and they retired to the Horse and Groom for lunch before each couple set off on their honeymoon. Walking into the snug was yet another homecoming. The three couples sat at a table beside the leaded bay window. The windows had been permanently covered for the blackout when they had last been there, so it was lovely to see the view out onto the village green.

Jess looked at her two friends, feeling a lump in her throat. Although Evie and May were yet to be demobbed, both planned to leave the RAF as soon as possible. 'Promise me here and now that we'll never lose touch,' she said, blinking back tears.

'No worries about that,' Evie said. 'In fact, we should pledge to meet at least once a year, whatever happens.'

'Agreed.' May gave an emphatic nod.

'I have news, though,' Evie said. 'I just heard from Somerville – they're offering me a scholarship.' Over the cheers of the others, she continued, 'Alex will still be in the RAF, of course, but he's going to apply for a posting near Oxford.'

'Are you starting in October?' May asked.

Evie shook her head. 'I doubt I'll be demobbed in time. No, I'll start next year. I'll get my maths degree after all.'

'Attagirl, Evie!' Jess raised her glass in a toast. 'With all the study you've done over the years, you should have earned your degree within a month.' She turned to May. 'What about you, May? Any plans?'

May's cheeks turned a little pink. 'Well, Peter's staying in the RAF, of course.' Jess nodded. Like Alex, Peter had served in the RAF before the war. 'I hope we'll all be posted close together. I'm staying in the WAAF for now.'

'What about your writing?'

'I'm coming to that. I've written some short stories I'm really pleased with. I'm going to start sending them to magazines and newspapers and see how it goes.'

'They'll be mad not to snap 'em up.' Jess was one of the few people May had dared to show her writing to and she had been impressed by the ease and skill with which May could weave enthralling stories. She had no doubt her friend would soon be in demand.

Then May clapped a hand to her mouth. 'Talking of newspapers,' she said, 'I nearly forgot. I read an article yesterday that might interest you.' She turned to Peter. 'Did you bring that cutting I gave you? Let Jess see it.'

Peter pulled a scrap of newspaper from his breast pocket and handed it over. Jess took it, puzzled, then exclaimed in surprise when she saw the headline. 'I don't believe it.'

'What?' Evie leaned across the table, peering at the paper.

'Read it out,' May said, laughing.

Jess cleared her throat and began. 'The headline says "Film actor flies to the Far East." The article reads: "Film actor Leonard Steele, whose latest film, *Knights of the Skies*, was released last month to great acclaim—"'

'Only because you were in it,' May said. The others murmured their agreement.

Jess grinned at them before continuing. Although her desire for an acting career was over, she had been thrilled by the warm praise her performance had garnered. She felt she could now leave acting behind on a high. She turned back to the article. 'Where was I? Oh, yes: "Film actor Leonard Steele, whose latest film, *Knights of the Skies*, was released last month to great acclaim, yesterday revealed he is retiring from acting to devote himself to service in the RAF. 'Working on *Knights of the Skies* opened my eyes to the sterling work of the RAF,' he said in an exclusive interview with our reporter. 'I now know my heart lies in serving my country. As such, I will be remaining with the RAF after the war.' He went on to reveal that he was preparing for a posting to the Far East and had no plans to return to acting.'"

Jess laughed. 'I can't help feeling his newfound desire for a foreign posting was due more to a desire to escape his creditors than to serve his country. Still, I wish him well.'

'Long may he stay there,' Milan said with a glint in his eye.

'Hear, hear. But enough about Leo. Let's forget about him.' Jess raised her glass again and looked around the small group. 'Here's to ties of love and friendship. However many years pass, however many miles lie between us, may those ties grow ever stronger.'

As everyone raised their glasses, Jess beamed at her friends. They had come through the war stronger than ever. Whatever happened, and wherever they went, she knew they would never truly be apart.

Acknowledgements

I've avoided writing acknowledgements for my previous books, not because I don't owe thanks to anyone for their help, but because I'm terrified of forgetting someone! However, with *Victory for the Ops Room Girls* being the last of the Women's Auxiliary Air Force series, I'm daring to take the plunge and write one for all three books.

Sadly there are not many left of the women and men who served in the WAAF and RAF during the war. However, I owe thanks to all who wrote accounts of their war years or contributed to the oral histories in the Imperial War Museum. In particular, I must mention Eileen Younghusband whose book, *One Woman's War*, brings her experiences as a Filterer Officer to vivid life, and I couldn't have written this book without it. Thanks also to Cosford RAF Museum, the Battle of Britain Bunker at Uxbridge and Bentley Priory Museum.

Writing is a lonely business at the best of times, and books two and three were mostly written during lockdown. Thank you to all my writing friends who helped keep me going and stay (relatively) sane, especially to all in the RNA Birmingham Chapter, my Apricot Plots buddies and the Wrekin Writers.

To my sisters-in-law, Jana and Katka, for all their help with the Czech language, history and culture. It goes without saying that any mistakes are all my own. I hope

Katka will one day be able to forgive me for the insult to Moravians in book one.

I also have to say a huge thank you to my agent Lina Langlee for her enthusiasm, dedication and being the best cheerleader an author could hope for. Also to Julie Fergusson for ably taking over during Lina's maternity leave. Finally, to editor extraordinaire, Emily Bedford and the whole team at Canelo, thank you for being a joy to work with.